ISSUE 3

Published by 404 INK

404INK.COM   HELLO@404INK.COM
FACEBOOK: /404INK **TWITTER:** @404INK
SUBSCRIBE: PATREON.COM/404INK

ISBN: 978-1-912489-00-8
Ebook: 978-1-912489-01-5
ISSN: 2399-1577

Managing editors: Heather McDaid & Laura Jones
Cover design: Cameron Foster

Printed by Bell & Bain

CONTENTS

HELLO.
IT'S US.
AGAIN.
THIRD TIME'S A CHARM.

It's quite weird to have reached the third issue of 404 Ink's magazine already. It seems just yesterday we were sat in a spare room formulating what our next literary move would be under the 404 Ink moniker. Probably because very little has changed, as we sit… in a spare room… formulating our next literary moves… under the…

The point is, one year on from 404 Ink's first ever publication, it's nice to look back and see how far we've come as a publisher, and it's even nicer to have people still along for the ride (hello) and reading the amazing writers we're lucky enough to have been able to publish in that time. We're continuously astounded at the talent that slides into our inbox. This little literary magazine has even been shortlisted at the 2017 Scottish Magazine Awards – how exciting!

So, what did this year hold?

In March 2017, we published our first book *Nasty Women*. It's been an unbelievable journey with a gang of incredible women we consider ourselves lucky to know, and the latest stop on this adventure was Ali Smith (author of Man Booker shortlisted *How to be Both* and many other amazing books) sending us this beautiful quote (more like poetry, seriously):

It means thought and grace at a pressurised time,
it means protest against the worst odds for a century,
it means ageless reassertion of community both international and local,
it means the world not going backwards,
it means a huge sigh of relief,
an arm round the shoulder.

It means vital spirit.

This sums up the most joyful parts of what we get to do. To have published something that means even an ounce of that to anyone is a very humbling feeling, and one we don't take for granted. Similarly, one of the highest compliments is that something you published made someone laugh out loud in a place where they ought not be laughing out loud.

Chris McQueer submitted a short story to Issue 1 of our literary magazine in 2016. It was surreal, Scottish and hilarious. He read at our launch party and we knew that we had to publish him again. We're quite lucky that he let us, because *Hings* is single-handedly the funniest book we have read in forever. Sharp, witty, observant. He is a testament to why we love publishing this magazine – you never know who you're going to discover.

We've been working on a book with rock band Creeper, and also signed two books from one of our favourite authors Helen McClory for 2018. You'll get to read a snapshot of her upcoming collection *Mayhem & Death* in these pages. Helen is one of the finest writers to come out of Scotland in the last few years, and we're very excited to be working with her.

We've got one more big project announced for 2018 so far, and that's *We Shall Fight Until We Win*. 404 have joined forces with one of our favourite publishers BHP Comics to bring out a graphic novel anthology celebrating a century of pioneering women to mark the centenary of women gaining the right to vote in 1918. Pre-orders will be available on Kickstarter in January, so stay tuned.

But back to this hefty magazine that you are holding in your hands (or light one if you've gone digital). Power felt like a fitting topic for the third issue. While it seems obvious that politics would play a key part in this, we've also managed to find plenty of wonderful literary worlds to escape into. Sunny superpowers? Sure. Finding power in slacking off? You got it. Poetry on Frankenstein and the electrical jolts that shoot him to life? You're set.

Beyond that, there are some truly powerful life stories that will make you think, or inspire. Exploring identity in video games, self-harm, suffering a stroke, and the radioactive vengeance of battling illness – a number of our contributors have truly put themselves on the page, and we're very grateful they felt 404 Ink was a place they felt comfortable to do so.

We thought to wrap up the year we'd dedicate more pages to book recommendations than ever before. It's not limited to books out this year, but the best books we've read this year. In a similar vein to much of the content of the magazine, it's a mix of excellent fiction and poetry, and searing non-fiction. Aptly, the power of people using their voices to tell their own stories which are so rarely heard is more vital than ever and publishers are realising that and helping boost them further.

We've also got a number of our authors including Chris McQueer and our amazing Nasty Women to recommend their picks of 2017. There's some goodies in there to make your to-be-read pile that little more precarious. Because who doesn't like book recommendations?

That's enough babble from us. Dive in. Power to you for picking up our literary magazine. We appreciate it. Always.

– Heather & Laura
Directors of 404 Ink

FIXED POINTS

FIXED POINTS

On the power of writing and words, feelings and truth

MEL REEVE

I hate writing. It has so much power and potential but always seems to take genuine moments and feelings and warp them into something else. To write you have to be definite, you have to choose the words to use but there can only be so many. How can I express what any of this is like? That's supposed to be the mark of a good writer, to be able to explain feelings in a way that allows the reader to understand. All I feel is overwhelmed by the vast expanse of choices I have to make – a permanent decision on what something is when, really, it is always so many more things.

I hate writing. It takes something intangible, precious and wonderful or awful, and makes it blank. Every reading will always be different, we all take our own experiences and viewpoints and project them onto the words written by a stranger (even if it is written by our very best friend), assuming we understand, but it is never enough. Language is a cage, to be fought against and briefly tamed at best, but never defeated.

I think about this as I am walking down the street, drinking 7up, wearing my favorite denim jacket and sweating a little because it is unexpectedly warm. I'm almost home, so I keep the jacket on. My keys knock against my leg. There is a partial solar eclipse. I cannot see it because it is too cloudy. It still feels important. I kissed someone on the mouth a few minutes ago and my lips still feel warm. My chest is filled with hope. Today has been hard and it is starting to feel better. The music playing on my headphones swells and fills my ears. There is a brief moment where I expect everything to stop. I imagine a camera panning away, the screen going black in a cinema. I can see the viewer, satisfied by this resolution. This is an ending. I'm a writer, so I know that.

But the seconds tick by and I am still here, the song ending, my heartbeat echoing in my ears instead of music and the sun moving on in the sky.

All writing is finite. We know there will be an end. We are trained to recognise the particular shape of a storyline in films, books, songs and even newspaper stories. Everything is stretched into this pattern. At university I was taught how

Beowulf feels strange to our modern tongue because it doesn't fit the standard arc of a story we are used to. The shape of this need hasn't always existed in the same form, but it's certainly been here in some way or another, I think, it must have been. What else are cave paintings if not a story? Perhaps it is too romantic to imagine those early humans using cave paintings to create a narrative of their muddle existence, but it seems a little possible to me.

The line of the arc has changed, from daubings on walls, to Beowulf, to Hollywood movies, but it's always been there, I think. It is human to find importance in anything and it is human to want to share it, but we will never manage it perfectly.

When I write, I take the things that have happened to me and I shape them, like wet clay, into a story with a beginning and an end. Part of that process is the bit where I am living and having experiences. So, I am shocked a little when the perfect ending is created as I walk towards my flat under the solar eclipse, and I continue to be. I want to walk out of shot in this film, for the music to swell and fade, for peace and silence to reign and for my story to end. But it doesn't, it can't. I am not my story. I am not the words I wrote this minute or last year. These words are too slippery, never enough, never quite enough. I am walking down the street in my denim jacket, bubbles fizzing over my just-kissed lips, under a partial solar eclipse – a perfect moment made imperfect by the fact it carried on.

I will not write of what happens next here, maybe I will somewhere else. Because as much as I feel restricted, defined and constrained by words, I am also made free by them. I cannot control what you see when you read this, the colour of my jacket will never be quite right, the taste of that drink will be different to you. But I can be true to myself, I can get better at explaining how terribly complicated it feels just to exist, maybe one day I will get close, I will hope for nothing more.

And I can write an end for myself for today, and I choose this one;

I am standing beneath a solar eclipse, refreshed and recently kissed, in love and with a heart opening wider to the world. There is so much out there for me to learn and feel and write, and I am made joyous by potential for the first time in so very long.

I walk into the distance, turning a corner and out of your line of sight.

STUCK

VERONIQUE KOOTSTRA

Breathe in. The smell of Serrano ham and mustard. Yesterday's sandwich bag. Breathe out. Zoë sits in the corner facing the metal doors. She stares at the number eight. It blinks like a nervous child who's just been told off by a stranger. Breathe in. A panel light above her head flickers before giving up. Breathe out. She ties a knot in the sandwich bag. Her air captured. If she dies that will sort of be her last breath.

She should have taken the stairs but her new heels have reduced the blood supply to her curled toes. Maybe it's karma getting back at her. But Gina shouldn't have left her Jimmy Choos in the office.

She empties her bag onto the rough carpet tiles. Strawberry lip gloss, a can of gold spray paint, used chewing gum wrapped in a receipt, two sets of keys and a home knitted balaclava. When she first searched for a pattern on the internet, images of a sticky, apparently Turkish, pastry with nuts and honey came up. The wool has started to unravel.

She points her nose at her armpit. Sour like an unrefrigerated jar of pickles. Twenty-five hours since she had a shower. Twenty-three hours since Mr Fisher made her redundant. It's only fair that she destroyed his investment for a care-free retirement. If anything she enhanced his Mondrian with a gold sparkle.

The metal contraption judders. The numbers above the doors light up one after the other as it approaches the ground floor. She kisses the inflated sand-wich bag. An alarm howls; the soundtrack to her deed. Breathe in. She pulls the purple garment down over her chin. The loose thread rests on her shoulder. Breathe out. Zoë takes off Gina's shoes, uncurls her toes and waits for the doors to open.

A LIST OF POSSIBLE PROJECTS CONCEIVED WHILE WORKING AT YOUR SHITTY OFFICE JOB

A LIST OF POSSIBLE PROJECTS CONCEIVED WHILE WORKING AT YOUR SHITTY OFFICE JOB

ROSS MCCLEARY

1. Write a story while walking to your shitty office job. The first word of the story begins with the letter A. The second word of the story begins with the letter B. The third word of the story begins with the letter C and continues in this way until you reach Z. The journey from A to Z is a loop. Return to the beginning. The twenty-seventh word of the story begins with the letter A. Progress the story until the loop has been completed 26 times. On the 27th loop remove the word beginning with A from the sequence. On the 28th loop remove the word beginning with B from the sequence. On the 29th loop remove the word beginning with C from the sequence. Continue this process until there is only one letter left. The last word of the story begins with Z. The story has 1001 words. It is about a war. Memorise it.

2. Update Raymond Queneau's *Exercises in Style* for the Internet Age. Styles included: Vice article, Emoji, Downfall Parody, Blue Screen of Death, Trolley Problem Meme, Pitchfork review.

3. Sculpt a lipogrammatic short story. The missing letter is 'E' just like *La Disparition* by Georges Perec. It is about a unicorn that tricks the narrator into the middle of the road where they are then hit by a car. The story is about a unicorn is because 'a unicorn' contains all the main vowels apart from 'e'. There are other reasons. They do not matter.

4. Find a poem in the can of alphabetti spaghetti you have for lunch. Pour the contents of the can into a bowl. Fork each letter one by one into a second bowl and write down each one as you go. Rearrange the letters you have found into a poem. Eat your words.

5. Devise a story in which a second story emerges when you rearrange the words into alphabetical order. The trick to this one is, of course, that the alphabetical story must be written first.

6. Develop a bad attitude at your shitty office job out of boredom.

7. Use Microsoft Excel to create a random poem generator. Fill the database with the text of the Book of Revelations from the Bible. Keep hitting refresh until you have written enough for a short pamphlet.

8. Present to a conference a new alphabet. The new alphabet is designed to articulate the feelings of guilt and doubt and anguish that you are incapable of describing in actual human words.

9. Sketch out a short story. Choose ten of the most frequently used words. As the story progresses replace these words with different words, words with different implications. Allow these new words to occupy the same space and convey the same meaning. A second story emerges but its meaning remains the same.

10. Master a writing constraint in which the text can only be considered successful, correct, if a stunt car driving along the top of the letters is able to make it to the end.

11. Purge any unintended enthusiasm for your shitty office job from your body. There isn't much but it is there.

12. Draft a play about a support group for ex-secret service agents.

13. Tell one lie every day in your shitty office job. Consider this practice for being on stage.

14. Pitch to a publisher The Penguin Guide to Conspiracy Theories.

15. Replace all the onomatopoeia in a story you have written with the names of recently deceased celebrities.

16. Refuse to accept that the eight hours you spend in your shitty office job should be considered anything other than a total waste of time.

17. Put pen to paper: write down the first 10 letters you see on number plates on the walk home from your shitty office job. These are the first letters of each word in a new poem. Loop through the letters in order until there is nothing left to say.

18. Listen to a poem without word or sound.

19. Fashion a story using the 1000 most common words found in the comment section under articles published by the Daily Mail.

20. Conceptualise your escape from your shitty office job.

21. Make a concrete poem using the words you avoid using to prevent conspiracy theories coming up in conversations with your colleagues.

22. Shift the words of a poem you have written around the page until the curve of the letters and the spaces between words bend into the shape of a heart.

23. Complete a policy paper at your shitty office job suggesting that the Police be renamed Power Bastards. Shrug it off when your manager tells you this was an inappropriate use of your time.

24. Polish up a piece of cultural speculation that is sitting inside a drawer of your desk. The hypothesis is simple: *Sex in the City* is a ghost story.

25. Tweet negative comments about your shitty office job until the HR manger brings them to the attention of your boss.

26. Type out a prose poem in the style of Google Map directions. The directions will direct the reader to a place where they are no longer hung up on their last break up.

27. At your disciplinary hearing speak only in rhyme. They will discuss your tweets but also your attitude and how much time you spend playing with your phone. The nature of your contract means that, when they fire you, they do not have to give you prior warning. It hurts for around half an hour as you panic about money but it will be okay.

28. Become the writer-in-residence on a cargo ship.

29. Figure out a way to become the writer-in-residence on a ghost pirate ship.

30. Through breaking and entry if need be become the writer-in-residence in an abandoned cinema.

31. Script a one-act play using the format for answering competency interview questions as a constraint upon the dialogue.

32. Endorse people for Poetry on LinkedIn. Endorse people for Natural Horsemanship on LinkedIn. Endorse people for Crime on LinkedIn.

33. Grow a hedge maze in your garden out of boredom.

34. Sign on at the job centre. Attend their meetings every two weeks. Speak with confidence, dazzle them with your enthusiasm. Double down on your art instead of job applications. You will worry a lot but you will feel better.

35. Craft a diary delineating the paranoias of being alone in your flat during the day. Write of your fear of assassination, kidnap, and a premature death. All things which are more likely too occur because your neighbours have jobs and aren't at home during the day. That sort of thing.

36. Send short stories to prospective employers instead of your CV.

37. Perform found poems composed of the stupid questions they ask you at the job centre.

38. Breach confidentiality by stealing official documents from the job centre and project them onto walls in abandoned buildings.

39. Place job adverts on Gumtree for jobs you would kill to have. It does not matter that many of these jobs do not and cannot exist.

40. Beg the British Lawn Tennis Association for funding to paint the courts of Wimbledon so that they resemble the paintings of Mark Rothko.

41. Score a piece of music which sounds the same whether you play it forward or backwards.

42. Play a sound recording of football fans cheering and jeering during a game when there is no one in the stadium.

43. Fund the designing, writing, and recording of a song that deteriorates with every listen.

44. Sense out a story about a businessperson who finds a seed from the Tree of the Knowledge of Good and Evil. The seed is planted but the world, unlike the innocence within the Garden of Eden, is plagued by the complexities of moral relativism. Strange things happen but, then again, strange things happen all the time anyway. They try and fail to link the eating of the Fruit with the changes in people's behaviour.

45. Imagine choreography unhindered by the limitations of the human body.

46. Draw blueprints for a human black box recorder which can be placed underneath the skin.

47. Engineer a radar which can track people using their DNA.

48, Film vignettes composed entirely from small talk observed at art galleries and conversational failures witnessed in bars. Post the videos to YouTube.

49. Create a deck of Top Trump cards for Literary figures.

50. Patent a dummy for babies that, when held to their mouths, turns their cries for attention into the sound of laughter.

51. Fantasise about a WWE Pay-Per-View event written by Philip Roth.

52. Do a spoken word rendition of John Cage's 4'33. Perform it during a five minute spot at an open mic night.

53. Build a hotel. Fill it with ghosts.

54. Edit your memories until they closer resemble a work of fiction rather than an autobiography or memoir. Write down everything you remember and everything you have ever done.

Converse with someone online. Someone who saw one of your fake Gumtree adverts. Listen as they tell you about how they took one of the ideas and ran with it. It has become a successful venture. They tell you they would like to meet you. They provide coordinates. You discover the coordinates take you to the hedge maze in your back garden. When you reach the centre you find three people sat behind a long wooden table. They usher you forward and ask you to take a seat. You sit down. A job interview begins.

GIRLS JUST WANT
TO HAVE THUNDER

GIRLS JUST WANT TO HAVE THUNDER

JANE FLETT

Some men like to take a beautiful girl and hide her
from the world. Some fools believe in towers.

Well, if you really believe my long hair's your ladder,
I guess you've never seen my tights.

If you're crawling up anything, it's to the glory hole.
If you sever your feet on the way, I don't mind.

Whisper it: my cunt's the Hadron collider. My knickers
faster than the speed of light in Switzerland.

Last night we found negative matter. We posed
the thought experiment. We didn't mind.

The tower came down.

Some men don't understand what it means to say
her body is an axe. These men are slivers of glass

you won't see until they're stuck in the flesh
of your foot. Then, ladders don't matter anymore.

Listen: you can be the lightning or you can be
the people falling. You can make her tiny

or you can both be storm clouds, rumblestruck
and kabang. What would you rather?

Are you under the tablecloth yet?
Are all the crystal glasses still standing?

SUNLIGHT

SUNLIGHT

STUART KENNY

I fucking knew it. I knew something was up. It must've been going on my whole life. I just hadn't realised what was happening before. That may sound slightly ridiculous, given the extremity of the situation, but how was I to know that I was capable of doing something that I didn't even know existed until roughly 35 minutes ago?

Thank fuck I took Standard Grade Biology. Don't get me wrong, I was also initially of the viewpoint that staring at the centre of a cactus for three weeks would be more or less shite, but man, I could not have been more wrong. Most important class of my life. Mr. Boyd, you beautiful man. Metaphorically speaking, of course. He still looks creepy as fuck. Pretty sure he's had the same bit of kale stuck in his moustache since I got put in his class eight months ago. And I'm also fairly certain he's the kind of guy who plays chess against his own computer when he gets home at night. Still, fair play to the boy for today's lesson. Really changed the game.

I've got it all straight in my head now. I've even managed to work out how I hadn't worked out that I could do it before. I mean, how do you know you've got a special power if you've had the thing your whole life? And besides, think about it. Photosynthesis in Scotland? Sometimes you don't even see sunlight for seven months at a time in this country. Not here in Edinburgh, anyway. So even if you can photosynthesise, for the vast majority of the year you're pretty much just a regular punter; the rarity of the sun in the Scottish capital being a point perfectly demonstrated by the fact that the entire city acts like they're in some kind of Caribbean paradise anytime the weather forecast does head north of 15 degrees, bearing down on the Meadows in one monstrous half-naked mob, spontaneously combusting barbeques and hula hoops and dripping sweat and cultural appropriation as they get ready to settle in for the weekend. I'm no stranger to the meadows either, mind you. Call me one of the mob. I love those days. But I do always notice that after clearing out the frozen sausage isle at the Sainsbury's at the top of Middle Meadow Walk, I seem to always – always – have had eyes far bigger than my appetite can handle. Everyone else will be munching away when the food comes off the barbeque and I'm barely able to eat a thing. It makes sense now, of course. Now I know that I've been synthesizing nutrients from carbon dioxide and water this entire time. Since day one. No wonder I was already full.

It was so obvious when I realised what was going on. I love the sun. I always feel better on a sunny day. Before I just thought it was because everyone loves the sunshine, and as such it put somewhat of a skip in my step, but now I know it's because the sunlight actually puts my body in physically better shape – because I drag in all those nutrients from the sunlight, see. Literal human photosynthesis. It's spot on, this. It's like getting your five a day and seven glasses of water all at once just from kicking about on the streets for a bit.

We went on a family holiday to Malta last May and I was actually on form the entire week. Not hungover once. And I even had four beers one night. I actually never get hangovers in the summer at all. And I always eat more when I'm drunk too, which is always when it's dark outside. Thus, no sunlight scran available. Thus, no photosynthesis possible. Thus, the need to eat actual real people food. It all makes sense, see.

I hope I can control it though. One of my only concerns is that now I know I am capable of photosynthesis my mum will be raging because I won't be able to eat any of the meals she cooks me because I'll be full with all that sunlight. I know you're probably thinking that if it wasn't a problem before it shouldn't be one now, but the thing is I didn't know I could do it before. Now I know, think how hard it'll be to resist. Imagine if the sky was literally formed from your favourite food – like that film about the meatballs – and you had access to it all of the time. And you never gained weight from it no matter how much you ate. It's the dream. Mum would not be happy though. Actually no idea how she's going to take this news. "Mum, sunlight is my bread and butter now. Literally. I don't need you to cook for me anymore."

I can't envision her taking me too seriously to be honest, though, and who can blame her? She's still not fully come to terms with my ability to talk to dogs. I can't hear what they say back, of course, but they definitely know what I say. Learned about that one from Mr. Boyd a few years back as well. Mum kicked off at parent's night after I told her that. This photosynthesis one should prove a lot more useful than the dog one though. Especially after Keith got hit by a bus last week. Keith the dog. Not Keith my dad. I named the former (late and great) after the latter (punctual and easily agitated). But dad's fine. Keith, the dog, is not fine. Keith the dog got hit by a bus. No dog to talk to anymore.

My thought process on this one though is that photosynthesis should save my parents money, and even mum can't argue with that. Mum and dad have been bickering about money a lot recently, see. We even had one of those family domestics down the local pub the other week. A bucket list moment if ever there was one. But this could sort that. Just one less mouth to feed, isn't it? Think about it. I genuinely do not need food at all anymore. Not if it's sunny. All I have to do is go outside and… well. Actually, I'm not quite sure about the logistics of it yet. I guess I've been doing this for ages accidentally, so it can't be that hard. I'm quietly renowned in our circles for talking a lot, so my best guess is that it just starts itself up when you've got your mouth open outdoors. Maybe you have to really tense or move your mouth around a bit. Which seems simple enough. Kind of just like eating like a normal human being, but nothing goes into your mouth. It all just happens for you. I wonder if I'll still get to go to the toilet if I go full-time photosynthesis. Will I literally shit sunlight? Oh my God. See if I start literally shitting sunlight when I get into this, I will be so happy. That would be unreal. This is my reward for being vegan for the past eight days. Sunlight coming from where the sun don't shine. Imagine. Nah, this is too much. I need to try this now. I need to figure out how this all works. This is class. This is actually the best day of my life. I'm going to go get myself some nutrients. This is amazing.

Across the road, Ted put his mug of tea back down onto the coaster and rose from his chair as he heard the opening of a neighbour's door. He drew his living room curtain back just enough to create a spyhole and saw, exactly as he'd expected, the teenage boy from number 38 standing on the lawn opposite his, for the third successive day, with his mouth open, head tilted back and drool physically dripping down his face. Strange kid, Ted thought. Still, at least he's outside. It was a beautiful day, after all.

ALTERNATIVE TRUTH

JUSTICE AND THE

AMERICAN WAY

ALTERNATIVE TRUTH, JUSTICE AND THE AMERICAN WAY

JONATHAN MACHO

The Agent entered the aircraft hangar and made his way towards the cell. The small, flat-packed structure was the only thing occupying the immense space, with any shuttles, or whatever was normally stored in there having been cleared out in preparation. The scientists employed at the base weren't exactly comfortable with how their facilities had been co-opted for the duration, but when the President's men came calling, you had very little choice in the matter, regardless of your… personal feelings about the man himself. As the Agent approached he could swear that, despite the cell being entirely encased in lead, windowless and dull, he could see a slight green glow seeping from it. He could hear the buzz of the machine on top, the Green-K Generator as they had called it, building as he got closer.

His colleague, stony faced as ever, waited not far from the cell door. He was patted down in silence – a precaution, he knew, nothing personal. It wasn't so much that he was compromised here, everyone was.

He paused outside. He could clearly see the green now, slipping under the doorframe. He couldn't quite muster the courage to enter. 'How has he been?' he asked his colleague, unsure if he was simply stalling or trying to salve his conscience already.

'Quite alright, thanks,' a voice came from inside the cell, just loud enough to be heard. The Agent froze, barely managing not to jump. To his credit, his colleague didn't flinch. 'The lead stops me from seeing you,' the voice went on, 'but nothing can do much about the hearing I'm afraid. Come on in. I imagine we've got a bit to talk about.' The Agent took a moment to gather himself, wiped the sweat from his brow and, with a nod to his colleague, entered the room, closing the door behind him.

After his eyes had adjusted to the green glow emanating from the ceiling, the Agent allowed himself a moment's consideration. He'd never seen the Man or anyone like him up close before. In all honesty, his feelings were mixed. In many ways he was just like he'd seen on TV and in the papers. He was well-built, obviously – he could leap tall buildings in a single bound, and that requires some muscle. The red, yellow and blue of his suit were mottled by the green, just like everything else, but the symbol on his chest still stood out, like a flag, a statement of intent. His hair, unbelievably, even ended in that little kiss curl.

On the other hand, despite knowing that he was being weakened by the green, the Agent was taken aback by how… Human the Man looked. His eyes weren't glowing red. His chin didn't stretch a foot away from his face. There was no aura around him, no halo behind his head, and his cape didn't blow in some ethereal breeze. When he offered his hand to the Agent, despite the gravity of the situation, it was just a hand like any other. He shook it, and was both amazed and relieved to find his hand was still attached afterwards.

The Agent took a seat opposite the Man, his chair scraping noisily across the floor in the silence. The buzz of the machine was quieter in here, but still persisted in the background, and something inside it gave off an artificial, ozone smell. He found the atmosphere uncomfortable, and couldn't help but wonder how the Man felt about it, with his senses so heightened, despite his calm, even friendly exterior.

The Agent cleared his throat, making a show of flicking through the documents in front of him. Usually this would be to intimidate the prisoner, but today, he was just buying time to regain his nerves. 'Right, mister…' That was a bad start.

'No need for the Mister. I imagine you know who I am,' the Man said. The Agent was just grateful he didn't point at the symbol to emphasise the point. 'What should I call you?'

'Agent, I think,' he replied, trying to take back some power, not that the prisoner seemed to be anything but cooperative. 'Best to keep this formal.'

'Fair enough,' the Man said.

'Do you know why you're here?'

His smile saddened slightly. 'You're sending me home.'

'That's correct.' The Agent consulted his papers. Phrasing was everything here, even if the administration seemed to have forgotten that. 'You are here at the behest of the President of the United States as we organise your deportation from our sovereign nation and return to your point of origin. You are entitled to a final hearing and clarification of this ruling which I have been empowered to carry out.' The Agent met the Man's gaze, and was proud that he didn't waver. 'Do you understand?'

'Oh yes,' he replied. 'Although, I do want to offer a clarification of my own. You guys do realise my home planet was destroyed, don't you? That's why I was sent here in the first place. You're sending me back to nothing.'

'That's why this arrangement is… Different from the norm. We haven't had to return someone to a place with absolutely no structure to receive them, let alone somewhere…' He cleared his throat. 'Extraterrestrial before. However, the President has deemed it necessary due to the previous actions of your fellow… Nationals, that any person in America from that locality should be deported immediately.'

'I'm not sure Nationals is the right word, but I understand,' the Man said. 'Can I just ask which actions you're referring to? The attacks from my world's General? Or those of the robot created there, the one with the habit of sticking cities in bottles?'

'Well… yes.'

'And does your paperwork mention who stopped all of those criminals?'

The Agent made an effort not to check. 'That's beside the point. You yourself named terrorists who attacked US soil who came from your planet. Your actions don't change that.'

'I'm not just talking about me. My cousin has saved countless lives during her time on Earth. Heck, you should meet my dog. They both came from my planet. Are you going to ship them off too?'

After a moment, the Agent said, 'I'm not empowered to give that information.'

'I understand. It can be frustrating when you don't have the right powers, can't it?'

'Look we're not saying everyone from your home is a supervillain, just – it's better to be safe than sorry, right?' As soon as he had spoken, the Agent regretted it. The Man's calm rebuttals were throwing him off his game. He was a professional. It was time he started acting like it.

The Man didn't seize on his blunder, but simply added: 'I cannot approve of any decision than deems a whole group of people culpable for the acts of a few.'

There. An opportunity to turn this back to his advantage. He had his in. 'So, you're saying you could never pose a threat to the American people?'

'No,' he replied simply.

'And what about their President? You have been seen to oppose his policies and act against him on more than one occasion.'

The Man raised an eyebrow. 'Such as?'

'You and your… Colleagues were seen accompanying protestors during marches against the President. You, the Amazon, the Bat…'

'There were kids there, passionate young people trying to put across what they believed,' the Man explained simply. 'We thought it was important to keep an eye on them, make sure it all went okay, and let them know they were safe to express those beliefs. You really shouldn't try to politicise us.' He smiled then, despite himself. 'Then again, Diana was particularly interested in the Women's marches…'

'Exactly my point,' the Agent said. 'You say you can't be politicised, but everyone has a bias, an opinion. You've already told me some of yours. And you're earnestly telling me you're not a threat to this administration?'

The Man didn't even stop to think. 'Yes.'

The Agent smiled for the first time. 'You're living in a dream world.'

'I've heard that one before,' the Man said, smiling right back.

'And do you acknowledge that you've already defied the laws of this administration?' When the Man look puzzled, the Agent added: 'After you and your colleagues were seen at the marches, the President made your unsupervised actions illegal for a time, until it was blocked in court.'

'Oh yeah, the Executive Order against Superheroes,' the Man said. 'He doesn't quite grasp the concept of vigilante justice, does he?'

'And you didn't operate during that time?'

'Honestly? I probably did,' the Man said after a moment's thought. 'But it wasn't a move to undermine the President. It was because people needed help.'

'If you're claiming you've never made such a move, we know that's not true.' The Agent checked his notes. 'You have spoken out against his comments on the press, for one. In that interview with the Planet.'

For the first time, the Man looked angry. 'Yes, well. I'm a... Firm believer in the free press.'

The Agent was proud of how cool he kept under the man's glare. 'You have friends who work for a national newspaper?'

'And I didn't appreciate how they, and their profession, were treated. I believe in the importance of honest, unbiased and fair news. They can do more good than I ever could.'

'And you honestly believe that?' The Agent was earnest.

'They can represent truth in a way that's difficult when you wear masks and capes. I know that it's not all black and white...' The Man paused, trying to find the right words. 'I've noticed that, in this difficult time, people are taking advantage of fear. I try to do the opposite. I think the press can play a big part in finding the truth behind the fear.'

'But you acknowledge that you have a problem with the President's behaviour here?'

'Do you?' His tone wasn't accusatory. He really wanted to know.

'We're not here to talk about me.'

'I guess not,' the Man said. 'Okay then. Yes.'

'But you still insist you wouldn't pose threat to the White House?'

'No, I wouldn't. I've got far more outlandish, over-the-top, ludicrous threats to deal with than – hm. Then again...'

'Careful!'

He smiled sheepishly, as sheepishly as someone his size could pull off. 'Sorry, couldn't resist.'

'You say you wouldn't interfere and then you say things like that.'

He was serious again. 'I wouldn't interfere. That's not what I'm for.'

'And what are you for, exactly?'

After a moment, and with another small smile, he said: 'I guess you could take some comfort from the fact that I've come from a pretty ludicrous place too. The idea that somebody with all the power would fight for the little guy and help those who need it. Every time.'

The Agent frowned. 'You sound like the President.'

He looked at him, smile gone. 'Troubling, isn't it?'

'And are you that idea?'

He thought about it again, then said: 'I try my best to be.'

The Agent believed him. 'And do you feel threatened by the President?'

The Man blinked, like he'd never even considered it before. 'That's a good question. No.'

'Despite your disagreeing with him? The position he holds? All of this?'

'I believe in people. I know they can hold their own. And take it from someone who's died more times than he's comfortable with: there's always a reason not to be afraid.'

The Agent looked at the Man sitting opposite him. He made a case for being so straightforward, earnest and simply good, but he could tell there was something there, a man beneath the icon. It was so strange to think that the figure in front of him had lived a life, experienced everything that made up a human being. Stranger still was the impression that the Man gave – that he was so desperately trying to put all of that aside, to just help whoever needed it, whenever they needed it, and be the icon they all thought he was.

'Can I ask you one more question?'

'Shoot.'

'Why did you come here? Why are you just going along with this? We couldn't have stopped you, let alone your friends. We've caught that reporter lady who interviewed you trying to sneak onto this base five times already.'

The Man's smile widened. 'Of course you did. You don't have to worry about any of them. I told them not to interfere before I turned myself in.'

'Exactly. Why would you do that?'

'Because it was the law.'

The Agent practically scoffed. 'You said it yourself earlier – you're a vigilante. You don't care about the law.'

'Of course I do,' the Man insisted. 'The law is vital. I ignored the President's orders before because people needed help. And don't get me wrong, you can send me wherever you like; as soon as someone down here, anywhere in this world needs me, I'll be there. I have to be.'

'Then what's the point of all of this?'

'The point is that I'm not here to stop you from doing your jobs, or the President from doing his. I'm here to help people regardless of anything and everything. If you all want to send me away, I'll just keep coming back. In the end I just have to have faith that one day you'll let me stay again. Can't it just be that simple?'

The Agent wasn't sure what to say. 'Is anything that simple?'

'All I can tell you is what I've learned to be true doing this job. Difference is what makes us stronger, not weaker; where you come from is not necessarily your home; and nobody can do everything, not alone, not even… Well.' He gestured to his chest, to the symbol. His meaning was clear. 'Anyone who claims they can…'

'What?' the Agent pressed.

'They're living in a dream world.' The Man was smiling again, but now it was mirthless.

The door behind the Agent opened. It was his colleague, sunglasses on, face blank. The Agent had almost forgotten where they were. 'It's time.'

'I understand.' The Man stood, offering his hand again. 'Thank you for your time Agent. I hope our conversation has proven to be helpful.'

The Agent followed his lead, and shook. 'Thank you, sir. And good luck.'

The Man let the Agent's colleague handcuff him, normally a pointless gesture, but their scientists assured them the green would keep him manageable until they had launched. As he was led out the door, the Agent saw him in full colour for the first time, sunlight catching the symbol in all its straightforward glory. 'Wait,' the Agent said, stopping them in the doorway. 'Is there anything you want to say before you go? To close out my report? A message goodbye for the President? The people?'

The Man smiled. 'Not goodbye. To be continued.'

CLOSED CIRCUIT

CLOSED CIRCUIT

CAROL STEWART

Spark!

Ingenuity   Malevolence

Reflected in the eyes
of those who mesmerize

Inspire   Incite

The man in the street,
his wife, his children,
the apprentice

Tradesmen   Torturers
Artisans   Warmongers
Healers   Killers

To react!

AFTER YOKO ONO

AFTER YOKO ONO

HENRY BELL

Watch the news
get up fifteen minutes late
remember to incline at 45 degrees
from the keyboard
in horror
become a chamfered edge
wear tight fitting clothes
uncomfortable shoes
pay attention to each pixel
focus your anger
self-medicate
imagine the sun
is getting larger
and larger
filling the sky
look at problems
really look at them
if you begin to feel dizzy
if your eyesight blurs
and you think you can see a person
at the other end of the internet
or sitting next to you at work
step back
have a drink
refocus your rage
and really look at those problems
pretend you know more than you do
doubt yourself
at an existential level

imagine that there is a storm
raging between you
and the person you are speaking with
you are both drowning
start a secret family
put too much salt on your food
make tea badly
take your favourite mug and smash it
fill your pillow with the pieces
remember that you are entirely alone
scream at a stranger
hyperventilate
listen to every noise in the night
the relentless settling of the house
the shouts of your neighbours
cut open your mattress
stay online
99% of internet users give up
before the real fight begins
do not quit
collect an armament of insults
remember that like a good spice cupboard
your abuse should be varied
be misogynistic
racist and transphobic
remember to breath
sound the insults out
and type in caps
punctuation may weaken you
if no one has mentioned hitler
mention hitler
if someone has mentioned hitler
tell them they are a cliché
cut all the flowers from next door's garden
throw them away
dig a hole in their garden and let the rain fill it
lie in that hole
seek out and ignore advice
drip with irony
silence dissent

take up smoking
regularly quit smoking
talk over women
press the palms of your hands
against a keyboard till your fingers are numb
let your instinct
guide your bloodless hands
lumpily across the keys
kill a small animal
try to pull things back to plan A
keep hydrated
coffee or whisky is best
attack a friend
ruin a joke
whistle loudly and tunelessly
mind your mortality
let it stick in your throat
every time you feel sad
take a stone from the park
and place it in your bed
boil water in a pankeep the heat on
let the handle melt
and the metal warp
breathe in deeply

I AM BULLETPROOF

KARYN DOUGAN

I can't use my Magic today because I have to save it.

If I didn't have to save it I would fly out of Miss Clement's window. I can hear birds chirping outside. They are happy that it is a sunny day and they want me to come and play with them. My bear, Tomo, is walking around Miss Clement's office and his throat is rumbling because he is angry. He doesn't like being in small rooms – he likes being outside. Tomo is a Sun Bear. He is made of sunshine and his fur is gold and he is always glowing. He sleeps in the playground when I am in Mr Lynch's class. Mr Lynch's classroom smells of chalk and books and paint. Miss Clement's office smells of old carpets and dead flowers, sort of like my Gran's sitting room but Gran always had biscuits.

Miss Clement has my solo talk in her hand. Her face is doing the same thing that Mr Lynch's did in class when their foreheads get wrinkly and they look Perturbeded. She looks at me and shows her teeth like a dog does when it is angry and wants you to go away. She tells me that Mr Lynch liked my solo talk and I got the highest mark in class. This makes me feel nice because it is Something Good I can tell Daddy. I am Doing Well and this might make Mummy happy.

Miss Clement asks me why Hannah hit me at break time. Tomo Bear starts to rumble again. He wants to eat Miss Clement but I do not want him to. Miss Clement would not taste very nice because she is old and probably tastes of medicine. Miss Clement must know why Hannah hit me. Mr Lynch must have told her the bad things Hannah's friends were singing. If I didn't have to save my Magic I would have made my fists burn with fire and blasted them with fire-balls. I could have asked Tomo Bear to attack them and he would have ripped them apart with his claws or chewed them to pieces but we would have gotten into trouble because Daddy says Two Wrongs Don't Make A Right. Daddy also says Think Before You Speak and Money Doesn't Buy Happiness and Women Can't Drive.

Miss Clement says she will Talk to Hannah's mum. Adults always think that

Talking stops things or makes them better but it doesn't. Like when Daddy says he will Talk to the doctors but nothing gets better. It always just makes people shout because someone Isn't Bloody Listening or is being A Stupid Arse.

I see Daddy's car drive into the car park. Our car is shiny and red, like a cherry. Cherries are my favourite thing but I am not allowed to eat them without Mummy or Daddy because they think I might choke on stones. But I can't choke. No one who is Magic ever dies from choking on things. They die from battles or because an evil witch has cursed them. I have never met a witch so I am not cursed. I used to think that Miss Clement was a witch but now I know she isn't. Miss Clement would die from choking because she is a teacher and not Not Very Interesting.

Miss Clement asks if she can show Daddy my talk but I know she is not really asking, she is Telling. Like how Daddy asks me to clean my room or go upstairs. I should have done a talk about when I killed the ogre in the shopping centre with my lightning powers and all the toys cheered and wanted to go home with me. Or when I defeated the giant squid with my ice swords in the swimming pool and the lifeguard let me go down the big chute as a reward.

I shouldn't have done a talk about Mummy.

Miss Clement asks me to sit outside in the corridor. This is where Bad Children sit when they are waiting to go in for a Punishment. I hope no one sees me sitting here because I have not Been Bad. But I must have Been Bad if Miss Clement wants to talk to Daddy in the office.

Daddy has showered and ironed his shirt today which is nice. Sometimes he looks like my sweetie wrappers when I find them in the couch. He kisses my head and looks at the plaster the nurse had to put on because I was bleeding. Daddy says he'll be Two Minutes and goes into Miss Clement's office. If it was An Emergency, I would use my super hearing to listen to what she is telling him.

Suddenly Tomo Bear starts to growl. Giant rats dressed as a marching band are coming down the corridor. Their teeth are sharp and slavery and their music is loud and scary. Their eyes are blood red and they are all squeaking a bad song that hurts my ears. I stand up but I am not sure what to do without my Magic. Tomo is glowing brighter. He is going to protect me. He roars and runs towards the rats who hiss and try to get away but Tomo slashes them with his big claws and burns them up with sunbeams from his eyes until they are all dead. I give Tomo a big hug and tell him that he is the best bear in the world and he pushes his nose into my neck to tickle me. I sit back down in my chair when Daddy opens the door.

There is something wrong with Daddy. He is not shouting at Miss Clement but it feels like he is. I don't like it when Daddy is Not Shouting. It is worse than Shouting because it means that Daddy is really, very angry. I think I have Been

Bad, like the day I made the Monsters come.

On the way to Mummy, Daddy stops at the petrol station to get flowers because the Damn Florist is closed on Mondays. He lets me hold them because I am a Big Girl. Tomo Bear chases the car as Daddy drives. I wish I could get out of the car and run with him. I could open the door and run faster and faster and faster until I am Speeding of Light. None of the other cars would hurt me if they bumped into me. Even when people at my school push me I never get sore. I am bulletproof and nothing can hurt me.

Daddy parks the car and we walk over to the big doors. The bad smell is there as soon as the doors whoosh open and Tomo Bear stays close to me because he knows I need to be brave.

Everything is shadowy in here. The walls are mustard yellow, like someone has been sick everywhere. Sometimes there are people walking by and I get a bit scared, even though I know that they are like Mummy. They are not bad and they are not going to hurt us. But sometimes they will shout or cry and I get a fright because I do not like that Mummy is in here and has to listen to them crying all the time. It will make her sad and I don't want Mummy to be sad anymore.

The big nurse I remember from last time is here. She is like the evil queen from Snow White but the queen wore a crown and didn't chew gum all the time. The nurse says we can't take flowers to Mummy. Daddy tells her not to be silly, and she says that it isn't silly, someone hurt themselves last time but Daddy shouts Not To Talk Like That In Front Of My Kid. The nurse takes the flowers out of my hands.

Tomo Bear roars and stands on his back legs until he is as tall as a tree. I make fists to stop Magic bursting out of me. I am so angry that I make the ground shake like an earthquake. I hate this lady. More than witches, more than the kids who push me, more than Mummy's Monsters. I want to grow into a giant and stomp on her until she is crushed to death. They are Mummy's flowers and not the stupid nurse's and she can't have them.

Daddy puts a hand on my shoulder. He is telling me to Come On. Tomo Bear roars again but he follows us because he is a good bear.

We find Mummy in the same room as last time. She is in her dressing gown and slippers and is looking out the window. Tomo Bear walks over to Mummy and lies down at her feet. Daddy says Hi Darling and gives her a kiss and sits in the old pink chair beside her. His leg starts to bounce. I do not like Arriving because it is just as bad as Leaving. Mummy and Daddy always cry. Mummy is smiling but her eyes are all swollen and ugly and her nose is dripping. I show Mummy the petal I stole from one of the flowers. I tell her that the nurse took the flowers because she might hurt herself like the other lady and that I did a talk at school about how she fights Monsters and that she was in here having a rest but she would be home soon.

Mummy starts crying. I have made her sad again, like the day I was Bad. Mummy said it was time to go home but I wanted to stay in the park. I yelled with my Magic and the Dark Bit came out and went into her. That's how the Monsters found her.

It's my fault. I didn't mean to hurt Mummy. I didn't mean to bring the Monsters. I miss Mummy so much and I want to fix her so she can come home. Daddy is rubbing his eyes. I should try now.

I climb into Mummy's lap and put my arms around her shoulders. If I take the Dark Bit out, the Monsters will leave Mummy alone. I make my hands light up with sunshine and try to put it into her. But it doesn't work. She is still crying and her shoulders are rocking and I try harder but my sunshine won't go into her.

I cling to Mummy and make my whole body glow. My body gets hot like a computer does when it is working too hard. Tomo Bear is shining too. He is now brighter than the sun.

The sunshine makes the room look like it is a summer's day and if anyone looked into the room they would be made blind because it is so strong. I want it to go into Mummy. I want to make her better. The more bright I make it, the more dark she is. She is a shadow and I don't know how to put light into a shadow.

But I am bulletproof and Magical and I can save everyone.

DEARGAN

DEARGAN

MARCAS MAC AN TUAIRNEIR

Ged nach mi a bhios den aon bheachd,
's tu nad sheanamh an Taigh an Ròid,
a' liùgadh slighe tro dhroigheann
co-fharpaisean òraideach,

Cha b' urainn dhomh ach èirigh nam
thrèan-ri-trèan le gairm-aighir 's tu ri
spaidsireachd dhachaigh, feasgar.

Thionndaidh thu gar faicinn am broinn
liùchairt gìomach guamach,
duilleagan nan leabhraichean a' cagarsaich
dhìomhaireachdan sgeilpeach.

B' iad na faclan agadsa a spreig an
suim a chuir mi annad, an là sin,
gad fhaicinn, 's tu air smachd
a chumail air lasan tomhaiste.

Isean dearg air èirigh o
luaithre mo chuid aineolais.
Bha thu ceart sradag bheag a
chur, gu clis, ri clàs na truaille.

BANA-PHOBIITIGS

BANA-PHOILITIGS

MARCAS MAC AN TUAIRNEIR

Luchd-poilitigs, riamh nam faileasan
garbh-chumta, glèidhte an cèidse

glainne sgrìon an teilibhisein.
Guthan geallaidh fhalaimh air an rèidio.

Cha robh mi 'n dùil d' fhaicinn aig
mo ghuaillean; gaire air do ghnuis.

Bu mhor m' iognadh 's tu rinn suidhe
rim thaobh, deònach mo bharail-sa a
chluinntinn,

Fhad 's a rianaich mi mo smuaintean fhìn,
an loidhne boinnean leanna air
bòrd an taighe-seinnse.

Cò fear a thagaireadh nach màthair
an tè a bu fhreagaraiche
air' a chumail air an rìoghachd.

Boireannach rinn cleachdadh dh'èisteachd,
fhad ghlaodhraich ùranach amh.

SELF-HARM

TRIPTYCH

SELF-HARM TRIPTYCH

EVER DUNDAS

*** CONTENT WARNING: CONTAINS DESCRIPTIONS OF SELF-HARM ***

SEEKING YOUR ATTENTION: SELF-HARM

1996. I was chatting to someone in a club and I told him the Manic Street Preachers were my favourite band. "That explains those then," he said, pointing to my self-harm scars.

If he was trying to get in my pants he needed a new angle, a new line, a new collection of words that wouldn't leave me dismissed and punished for daring to show that which should be hidden.

Anyone who shows their scars can't really be suffering – if they were, they'd hide it. *She's attention seeking. She's only doing it because of that bloke in her favourite band.*

Years of depression and an intolerable situation reduced to copycatting – that cut deep. It hurt.

Followed by anger.

Indignation.

Then: "He was a wanker."

Years later, I'm willing to give him the benefit of the doubt – he simply didn't understand self-harm.

What it is.

What it does.

What it *achieves*.

How it feels (better than sex, drugs, rock 'n' roll).

My self of the now, my advice to MrBenefittedByDoubt – if you're chatting someone up, don't undermine them. They won't open up to you; their mouth, their cunt – sealed.

But what if I had been MissCopyingTheBlokeInTheBand?

I self-harmed before I knew who the Manics were. I self-harmed before I knew self-harm existed (The ego! Teenagers think they invented everything).

If I hadn't already discovered self-care through self-harm before I saw that beautiful infamous photograph of Mr Edwards, if I'd picked up the glass, the knife, the blade *after* I fell in love with the Manics, would that be such a bad thing?

Generations – razed in patterns of smoke and alcohol. A copy of a copy of a copy of a.

Violence towards others. Violence towards the othered. But not yourself – that way lies madness.

Self-harm offered self-relief. Relief of self. Relieved of signified self.

Self-harm let out a deep-red rage.

Self-harm kept me from the bridge, pills, rope, river.

I didn't copy the bloke in the band. Blood-letting and burning came first, the Street Preachers second. Self-healing, both. My teenage ego (it's only me, no-one else) took a blow gladly – when I saw that infamous photo of Mr Edwards (the opened up body: no lines here to read between, it's all clear) I knew I wasn't alone.

Teenagers. Can we read between the lines between us and them?

Dismissed in hormones, drama, rebellion. It's just a phase, they'll get over it. They're just attention seeking, they'll grow out of it.

Most people who self-harm hide it. What if they didn't? What kind of attention are they seeking exactly? (I can tell you now, it isn't the rage-inducing reaction from the bloke who failed to chat me up).

If they get help to cope, help to re-direct that burning, slicing, excoriating rage, then surely that's a good thing.

Why should we cover up our wounds and scars? Why is it shameful? Does it make you *uncomfortable*? We can't have that – cover up, bury it, and stand to attention with that stoic stiff upper lip. Do not re-direct that blood-red rage upon adult(erated) authority. Do not be a citizen. Do not be an artist. Do not read between the lines and do not write in bold. Do not carry your scars well. Do not take away the capitalist right to comfort and lies.

Capitalism funded by our boozing and smoking, but cutting open your skin comes free with your kitchen knife, your broken-open plastic razor, a sharp shard of a high from broken glass – delicious by-products. You adults, drowning in your rivers of booze, your fog of smoke. Are you coping? Or slowly dying?

This stiff upper lip contorted into a punk snarl – I am I am I am I and this is my body. My punk attitude came and went. I walked a stilted walk of uncertainty – I covered up. I didn't. I covered. I didn't. I covered. I didn't want to lose my means of coping, so covering up seemed the best 'choice'; should someone take this from me, what would I do but die? (You know not what you do – I'm the (post)modern Jesus. But I don't want this exit).

This is my gift to you. My collection of words, the complex reasoning and circumstances behind covering/not covering. To dismiss self-harm as attention seeking or copycatting – even if it *is* copycatting or attention seeking – is *cowardly*. To dismiss it means you don't have to deal with it. You can simply sneer.

I won't feel humiliated. I won't feel shame. I will smile (and snarl) and say, "I give you these words. I redirect this blood-red rage. I bestow upon you the benefit of doubt."

WHAT'S YOUR POISON-CURE? SELF-HARM AS SELF-CARE

I was sitting with an acquaintance, pleased to be wearing a short-sleeved summer dress, when he said, "What's that? Did you paint your arm?"

I looked down, surprised for a moment; my scars have become such a part of me I often forget they're there. I contemplated them; slivers of silver glinting in the sun.

"They're self-harm scars."

"I hope you stop doing that to yourself," he said.

What made this acquaintance think he had a right to tell me what to do with my body? With no awareness of my circumstances, no understanding of why I'd need self-harm.

"These scars are twenty years old," I said. "It isn't something I need to do anymore."

But if this had been twenty years ago?

I remember that feeling of panic that the one thing that was giving me control over my life was going to be taken away.

What is your motive if you tell someone to stop self-harming? Are you sweeping in to 'save them from themselves'? Are you erasing their agency with your good intentions?

I said, "You shouldn't tell someone to stop self-harming without an alternative in place, without support and care."

Engage in a dialogue. Listen to their story.

But to take away the one thing that may be keeping them alive?

"Self-harm," I said, "made me feel better, gave me control. It helped me cope. Self-harm was self-care."

He looked confused, so I said, "I wouldn't be here today, speaking with you, if it wasn't for self-harm. I wouldn't be alive."

"I'm glad you're here," he said.

He still struggled to understand how self-harm could be positive – it's counter-intuitive to most people, and self-harm is often mixed up with suicide attempts.

For your understanding and empathy, I give you the holy trinity of self-harm as self-care:

RELEASE

What happens when you have an intolerable situation, no way out, and no way to express emotions? A powder keg of suppressed rage.

I'd oscillate between two extremes: boiling anger followed by feeling nothing at all.

When I self-harmed there was a release of pent up rage that gave way to exhilaration. When cutting, the blood surfacing and flowing across my skin was bliss. Burning felt like electric bubbles travelling across my arm and bursting in my brain, creating euphoria.

When I felt nothing other than disconnection and alienation, self-harm was a means to feel alive again.

Self-harm is often misunderstood as masochism. For most people who self-harm, it isn't masochism at all. For me, it was never about 'enjoying pain'. Usually I didn't feel pain; when I did, it was about control.

CONTROL

What happens when someone spends their life feeling trapped and powerless? They wrest control from wherever they can find it.

The self-care of self-harm gave me something I had power over, gave me a sense of autonomy. When I self-harmed and I did feel pain, I was the one in control. While I 'owned' pain, nothing could hurt me.

Having had negative experiences of embodiment, self-care through self-harm felt like a positive engagement with my body. I didn't have control over the ravages of eczema but I could control self-harm; as people tried to take ownership of my body by telling me I was 'wrong', I could take back that ownership.

SURVIVAL

What happens when you're in an intolerable situation with no way out, and suicide is creeping its way in as the only option?

I was suicidal, but it was a battle – I didn't want to die. I kept suicide at bay by self-care through self-harm. At the time, it felt like the only alternative to suicide, as I had no other way of coping.

*

Now that I've outlined self-harm as self-care, let's deal with that binary we can't escape: positive vs negative.

There's widespread stigma and misunderstanding around self-harm, so I chose to write about the positive. I want to move away from the automatic reaction to self-harm as something negative, but without erasing that side of the narrative.

Self-harm isn't a long-term solution; while it might provide initial relief, it can often become a damaging coping mechanism that's difficult to give up. Many people who self-harm want to stop, but might not be able to find an alternative and it can get out of control (ironically, as it's often used to gain control). For some, self-harm can be an expression of self-hate and used as self-punishment.

But self-harm shouldn't be pathologised; it's an understandable coping mechanism in the face of difficulties. Pathologisation calls into question the person's agency, when their decision to self-harm may be perfectly rational. Of course, resorting to self-harm means there's something very wrong, especially if this is the only way someone can experience any power in their life – but they're not 'psychotic', 'disturbed', or 'sick'. They should never be castigated for choosing self-harm. Often, self-harm isn't the problem – it's usually a means to cope with something; that 'something' is the problem.

Here we have the failings of language. 'Self-harm' erases the care aspect. 'Self-care' erases the harm aspect. We need something in-between, something that encapsulates both at once, that isn't as emotive as 'self-harm'.

Even with altered language, will our society ever understand that cutting and burning can be self-care? I asked you for understanding and empathy and I gave you my holy trinity, my poison-cure –

Release.

Control.

Survival.

I've been to hell and back and I'm telling you this:

I'm glad I had self-harm. I'm glad I used it to cope. I'm glad I'm alive.

EMBODIED NARRATIVE – SELF-HARM AND SCARS

As you know, dear reader, I was sitting with an acquaintance when he asked about my scars. I went on to tell him I love my scars and he looked at me in disbelief.

How can anyone love scars?

You're making do because you can't do otherwise. If you could be rid of them, you would. Wouldn't you?

Non-normative embodiment is policed in everyday interaction.

Non-normative embodiment is open to interrogation; demands are made – justify yourself.

Let's turn that interrogation around – what is 'normal'? It's a construction, it has a beginning: with the emergence of statistics the 'average man' was born.

If there's an 'average man', there are Others who are placed in opposition.

'Normal' is what the scarred body is positioned in relation to, and as being unable to live up to.

'Normal' is a construction, a means through which to gain power.

I'm open to interrogation – opened up, like a cadaver on the autopsy table. I'm positioned as a problem, with the assumption of the classical unmarked western (white male) body as the norm. My non-normative body must be called upon to justify the breach of the normative, and must be brought into line.

I am categorised, pathologised – a means to organise, to fix the body so the body can be read; denying complexity, multiplicity, ambiguity and an on-going narrative.

My scars are beautiful.

I love that they've turned silver over the years, I love the way they catch the light. I'm lucky I appreciate alternative forms of beauty, I'm lucky I have friends who feel the same. Sometimes I forget our narrative is interrogated or dismissed. I forget that being happy with yourself and your body is not what society wants.

I don't feel ashamed of my scars. I don't think they're ugly and I don't think they should be covered up.

Let's interrogate this ugly narrative.

There aren't many people who feel the way I do, because it's not 'normal' – the body must be unmarked.

Yet the body has to be marked to be unmarked – 'nude' make-up, hair removal, botox, plastic surgery. The body must be a certain kind of beautiful. But if you're a certain kind of beautiful, why aren't you *more*? Why aren't you more like this? Or this? Or this?

Compare, despise, analyse, scrutinise.

The body must be this, the body must be that. The body is you. The body isn't you. The body is the body is the body. When we interrogate this word – (disem)'body' – it's clear it's a living death.

Men – we give you the sexualisation of scars. They prove your masculinity.

Women – you must be marked to be unmarked (nip and tuck). Your body must not have lived (childhood falls, sport injuries, war wounds, surgery, childbirth, accidents - erase it all).

My body cannot be scarred.

Sweet sixteen, someone says to me: "What about what your husband thinks when he sees your scars?"

What husband? Who is this man? A mythic creature whose demands I must accede to before he even exists, if ever. And here we are, stuck with this broken record of heteronormativity – my policed body must be feminine and I must be straight.

If my mythic future husband disliked my scars then he would not be my husband.

My (living) body is mine. It isn't *for* anyone.

I am mine. I'm not *for* anyone.

But no (hu)man is an island.

Do I need to erase little parts of myself because there's a dominant narrative I don't fit into?

What power do I have in the interpretation of my scars? What control do I have over their meaning?

My scars are beautiful.

My scars tell a story of survival. This body is not the living dead.

Why would I want to erase that narrative?

But now, here we are – that same binary: positive vs negative.

Does my positive narrative of scars silence your narrative? There are people who have scars who want to cover them, reduce them, erase them. Just because a body tells a story doesn't mean you need to accept it if it's painful or no longer relevant to you. My narrative is not judge, jury and executioner on yours. I only fight the *dominance* of erasure, the ease with which it's expected and accepted. We are mature enough to be able to embrace (not tolerate – *embrace*) multiple narratives. These narratives can speak to each other – we can hold this tension as if it were light as air.

My scars are beautiful.

My scars tell a story of survival.

I am alive and I am *living*.

There's power in these words. This is my truth – tell me yours.

SUPERVILLAIN

SUPERVILLAIN

SIOBHAN SHIELDS

Before the Mastectomy
The doctor injected wee
pieces of metal
into my breast
to mark the edge
of the malignancy.
I could smell oatcakes
on her breath
and she said
"Whoops!
I sent that one too far"
and I imagined that
wee Titanium bar
orbiting the tumour in my flesh
lost in the time and space of my breast,
like Sandra Bullock in Gravity
Spinning head over feet eternally.

Before the bone scan
the nuclear technician ran
radioactive tracer
through my veins
to seep into my bones
and make them glow.
Afterwards she said
not to hold any children or pets
in my lap
"because your bones
are radioactive."

So I edge away from children on the bus
using my bag to cover me up
and I think of what a great
Supervillain I'd make.
My superhuman powers would be;
ability to withstand great injury,
magnificent Titanium breasts
and my radioactive vengeance.

RINGS

RYAN ENDE

CHICAGO – 1996

Perched within the confines of the living room bay window, legs folded up and hugged close to her chest, Liz half paid attention to any movement from outside, half to the Bulls game her father had blaring from the television. He was content to sit forward in his recliner, occasionally spilling a bit of beer with any particularly emphatic gesticulations toward the screen, accompanied by derision hurled at the refs or the other team. She was content to wait out the result, as well as the arrival of her mother, from her nest. Such had become their tradition. After all, game nights when Mom was out meant a later bedtime, a privilege now accorded to her, being twelve and all. It didn't matter that today was an afternoon game, they took their places like normal.

"Oh, yes!" her father shouted, rising from his chair, pumping both fists in the air as though he himself had been on the court. "72 and 10! This is the start of another threepeat, I can smell it coming."

Liz was about to point out that the entire playoffs still lay ahead, but the click of the front door closing made its way to her ears. With Dad's loud distraction, she must have missed seeing Mom approach. Allowing her legs to slip free from their arm bondage, Liz stepped down out of the window and gracefully made her way to the hallway. Or she would have, had her legs not fallen asleep from the position they had been kept in. Using the wall for support, Liz took one slow step after another, trying to avoid the pins and needles as much as possible.

Mom sat on the small bench in the hall, head resting against the wall, eyes closed. She hadn't even gotten around to taking her shoes off. One hand cradled her side, the other dangling over the bench's edge. Liz limped over and crawled up beside her, nestling head against shoulder, drawing her mother's free arm around her. Liz began to trace the designs etched into the rings on each of her mother's fingers, starting with the pinky and working toward the thumb.

"I take it we won?"

"Mhm. They learned from losing last night."

"Good. Losing teaches more than winning." Mom flinched, jostling Liz to adjust her position.

"Everything okay, Mom?"

"Oh, yeah, just a little sore is all. Long day."

"There's been a lot of those lately."

"I know, baby. But someone's got to do it."

"Why does it always have to be you though?"

Mom let out a little laugh, then winced, and Liz could feel her other hand tighten against her side. "Some day, sweetheart, you'll understand."

"If you say so." Liz nestled in a little tighter, careful not to put any pressure on her mother's side. Her eyelids grew heavy as Mom gently stroked her hair.

"I'm not always going to be here," Mom said after several minutes, so quietly that Liz almost didn't hear it from behind the veil of looming sleep. "I pray it's yet some time away."

SOME TIME AWAY (JUST OVER TWO YEARS, TO BE PRECISE)

The tradition remained, all that had changed was Liz's positioning and Dad's lack of beer. She had grown too much to be able to hug her legs to her and adequately see over top. He had grown too many heart problems to be able to chug his beers and adequately keep living. She watched intently as the clock ticked down to zero and Dad exploded.

"Called it!" he shouted. "Threepeat! No other team will ever be as good as this!"

Liz uncurled from the window. "Yeah, yeah. I'll get something to celebrate with, you just enjoy your fortune telling skills a little longer."

There was a mostly empty half-gallon of milk in the fridge, but her eyes were drawn to the old bottle of champagne that had been sitting on top for at least five years. What the hell, her dad could handle one small drink, and today was a cause for celebration. A little alcohol wasn't going to kill anyone.

When she turned back toward the living room, champagne and glasses in hand, Mom was leaning against the door jamb. Blood dripped off her, pooling on the linoleum. Her face was a mess, almost unrecognizable beneath the dozens of cuts and bruises.

"M-mom?"

Her mother collapsed, but by a scant half-breath, the champagne bottle won the race to the floor.

THE WEEKS THAT FOLLOWED

"So sorry about your loss…"

"A rare woman, one of a kind."

"Do you need anything?"

"Liz, you doing okay?"

"Sorry about your loss."

"Such a shame, to lose a mother so young."

"What can I get you?"

"Dad, put down the bottle."

"She loved you very much."

"In the event of her passing, she wanted you to have this letter."

"Sorry about your loss."

"…Jordan's retiring again."

"Seriously, Dad, you need to stop drinking."

"Sorry about your loss."

"Your schoolwork is suffering, how can we help you?"

"Sorry about your loss, but…"

"I take it you haven't read that letter yet."

"She wouldn't have wanted to see things be this way."

"How much longer are you going to milk this?"

"We've all lost someone, you're nothing special. Get over it."

"Such a shame to see them this way. The death hit them hard, but still…"

"You really should take a look at that letter. Might bring you some closure."

"Everyone gets a little bummed out sometimes, you're not really depressed. Just sad."

"Feel free to say whatever you want in here, this is a safe space."

"You need to figure things out over the summer."

"Try to cheer up."

"Have a good summer."

ONE SUMMER MORNING

Liz stared at the white envelope and her name scrawled in her mother's handwriting across the front of it. It had sat there ever since she had been handed it, unopened, an oppressive weight growing more so with each passing day. Everyone wanted her to read it: her friends, the lawyer that handed it to her, family acquaintances, neighbors, her therapist. She had made attempts. The seal had been picked at, one half now pried loose. The edges of the envelope crinkled and creased, a result of being picked up and put down time after time.

"Screw it," she said to no one, grabbing the envelope and tearing through what remained of the seal. A neatly folded piece of paper, too small compared to its envelope, slid out across the desk, and Liz barely stopped it before it tumbled off and to the floor.

'My darling daughter,

I know this has been a difficult time for you, and I regret having to add to it. I am Signet, Hero and protector of the city. For over 200 years, our family has borne the mantle of Signet, perhaps even longer if some of the rumours I've heard are true. I am sorry I could not tell you myself, I had hoped for a different end than the one I likely came to. It falls now to you to carry on our family's legacy. The rings are yours; may they serve you better than they did me.

Always, and evermore, I love you.'

No sooner had Liz numbly set the letter back onto the desk than a clacking rattle approached her room. The door flung open, and through it bounced and rolled the ten rings her mother had always worn. She tried to stand and back away, but there was only so much space to do so, and the rings tracked her every movement.

Before she could react any further, one by one, the rings launched from the floor to encircle her fingers, fitting perfectly. A shudder, starting from the floor, worked its way through her body to her fingers – no, to her rings. They throbbed, thrummed, twinged, twanged. Warmth infused her, bore her onto a sea of calm assuredness.

Liz could feel the rings in her mind. Ten rings, ten powers to learn to unleash. Hers to command. They pulsed expectantly, waiting for her to act. The one on her left middle finger most brightly, cheerfully, calling to be used. Memory stopped her, of her mother frequently fiddling with that ring, a frown typically etched into her normally cheerful face. She couldn't place why, but she knew that was one ring's power never to tap into.

Dad stopped in the doorway, bottle in hand once more. His eyes lit upon the rings, and the corners of his mouth pulled down, a fury barely contained behind his gaze.

"Those were hers. Take them off."

"Mom wanted me to have them."

"I don't care," he said, stepping into her room. "Take them off."

"Put the beer down. Sober up. Get it together. Mom would be ashamed." Liz barely noticed how the right pinky ring seemed to glow just a little as she spoke. Her father's demeanor, however…

"You're right," he said, setting the bottle at his feet. "I'm sorry. They…they look good on you."

Liz waited patiently as he left, even waited until she could hear his feet descend the staircase, before leaping to close her door. Back pressed against the wood, she stared at her hands. What else was she capable of now?

A FEW DAYS LATER

The sledgehammer swung down at her, and Liz just barely rolled to the side in time to avoid taking it directly on the chest. As the head struck concrete, a small explosion burst from the impact site, the concussive force throwing Liz further away. She shakily regained her footing, readjusting the hood of her jacket to better cover her features. The man at the other end of the sledgehammer growled, dislodging the weapon from the crater with a jerk. He charged her again, leading his assault with the sideswiping hammer.

The hammer drove toward Liz's side, until a moment before it would have connected. Her body blinked out of existence, reforming behind the man. She punched out with her right hand, sending a visible ripple of force at his back. He recovered quickly, bringing the hammer in a spin at Liz's side. Her left hand interposed itself, and the hammer rammed into a shimmering half-dome of purplish energy. The force of the blow and subsequent exploding hammer-head still drove her back several feet and shattered her focus on maintaining the barrier. Sensing weakness, the man pressed his attack.

Liz managed to sidestep one overhead chop, dodge aside from the upswing, but could not get fully out of the way of the backswing. The hammer drove into the bottom of her rib cage, and the explosion rocketed her skidding across the ground, coming to a stop against the stairs leading into the nearby apartment building. A hole had been shredded into her clothes, and the now exposed skin blistered and burned. Liz tried to stand back up, but the act of doing so sent pain arcing through her torso, and she collapsed back onto the stairs.

She weakly held out her right hand, focusing into the middle finger ring. The hammerhead started to glow, red to yellow to white. The heat traveled down the haft to the man's hand, and he dropped the sledge. It nearly landed on his own foot, explosion sending concrete shrapnel across the sidewalk. The effort of concentrating through the pain to continue superheating the metal was too much, though, and Liz's hand dropped to her side.

Once the man had stopping shaking the pain out of his own hand, and noticing that his exploding sledgehammer had ceased glowing, focus returned to Liz. Hammer returned to hand. Snarl returned to lips. Liz couldn't help but start laughing, even though doing so wracked her torso with pain.

She took one last look at her ringed fingers. Stupid, to rush straight into testing herself, her new powers. She should have taken her time, trained and gotten a feel for this Hero business. "Someone's got to do it," her mother's words echoed back to her. "Some day, you'll understand." Too late now. Sledgehammer man was almost upon her, readying the coup de grace.

A pulse in her mind, vibration on the left middle finger. "Use me," it seemed to say, "I can save you. What other choice do you have?"

Had her mother had the same choice? What could be so bad about it, when the alternative was death?

The hammer arced up, both hands on the shaft, ready to deliver a final, crushing, explosive blow. Liz jabbed with her left fist, and from the middle ring shot a brilliant beam of light, twin intersecting rays weaving in and out from the primary one. It lanced through sledgehammer man, through a tree on the opposite side of the street, through an apartment building, and out into the sky. Everything it touched flashed to ash, and the hammer clattered to the pavement, the only thing left of the man that had held it was his ring finger still wrapped around the haft. Liz's ring shuddered and twisted, gleeful in its destructive premiere, and for a moment, Liz shared the sentiment, even desiring it, craving it, needing it to continue.

The moment passed. Never again. Some prices weren't worth paying.

A little bit of pressure from her right hand on her injured side sent a jolt of healing energy through her, knitting the broken ribs back together, at least to the point where she could move. She didn't completely heal everything. The pain would serve as lesson, that she still had much to learn before living up to her mother's reputation. Liz grabbed the hammer as well. A souvenir, and humbling reminder.

CHICAGO, PRESENT DAY

Liz carefully took down the hammer from where it hung on the wall, running her fingers down the haft. A small, almost unnoticeable splatter of dried blood darkened the head still.

"Signet, come on! The city isn't going to patrol itself!"

"Be right up."

Her fingers trailed across the hammer one final time before sliding it back onto its support brackets. The tenth ring shuddered and throbbed; Liz began to toy with it, twisting it about on her finger, tracing the etched designs. It was becoming harder to resist the temptation. She had thought looking at the hammer would help, but it only made it worse.

"Soon," the ring seemed to call.

Soon, she might answer.

MANIFESTATION

MANIFESTATION

DANIEL SHAND

The couple walked along the beach near night and ignored the ghost completely. It was easy to look through its veils and chains and see only the sunset and how it painted the far-off waves. This was because the ghost was an ancient spirit – pre-industrial certainly, perhaps even pre-agricultural – and now struggled to manifest. It had haunted the shoreline here for centuries, maybe even longer.

'Look,' said the young man. 'This is a perfect skimmer.'

The ghost watched him select a little grey disc from the beach and send it bouncing over the water.

'What did I tell you?' the young man said.

The young woman drew her cardigan in closer and agreed – it was a fine skimming stone.

The ghost scrambled in the sand for a while, trying to find a stone of equal thinness, of equal balance, but came up with nothing. Its claw slipped through the shingle, causing a tremor of frustration to pass through, and then when it looked up the couple were away down the sand. It flew to catch them.

'I just think it's time to think about it,' the woman was saying. 'We can't stay with your parents forever.'

'Mm,' said the man.

'Don't you think so?'

The ghost didn't care much for this kind of talk. In life, it had lived with its mother in her cottage, existing humbly, until Mother had passed from the bleeding disease. After inheriting the property, and intending to exist humbly, the ghost succumbed to the same illness within mere weeks. It had loved no one in life and died orgasmless.

'God is a lie,' it whispered. 'After death, there is nothing. Nothing.'

It flapped into the air and sprayed around black clouds, but the couple took no notice.

The man put his hands in his pockets and started to kick rocks. He said, 'It's the money though, how does that work?'

'It just does, doesn't it? Other people seem to manage. The baby's coming, you can't deny that.'

'Mm,' he said.

As time went on, your powers of manifestation waned. When the ghost took form now, it was insubstantial – a loose collection of particles and thought. If it could muster the power of speech, it mumbled obscure terms like *Spindle* and *Ostler*, which confused as much as frightened. The ghost recalled some of the scares it had pulled off over the years…

The gentleman in a ruff that fell from the cliffs…

That grubby gang of children, driven insane…

The succubussed vicar…

So many decades since anything of that quality. So long. The last time anyone had acknowledged the ghost, a man was king. The last time it had felt the rush of pleasure that came from causing fear…

Sometimes you wanted to…

The man put his hand on the woman's big belly and said, 'I know. I know.'

He looked up and saw the ghost, but to him it was merely a passing shade. He smiled dozily. He was planning baby things, the ghost imagined. A little wooden bowl and spoon, a rock-horse, woollen leggings.

Sometimes you wanted to be seen.

The ghost transformed into a crab and threw itself down the woman's throat, holding its breath against the rank heat of human flesh. It went crawling through the corridors of mucus and organs until it found the chamber it was dreaming of – the infant sac.

The foetus saw nothing with his closed eyes but felt the ghost's presence. He vibrated *Hello*.

Hello, the ghost vibrated, and the two fused in a pulse.

Outside, the woman was complaining of a feeling of unease. She was cold and wanted to return to the holiday home in the village. The man helped her walk over the stones and shingle and onto the embankment.

'I can feel it kicking,' said the woman. 'It's so strong.'

GHOST TOUR

GHOST TOUR

SIM BAJWA

"I'll tell you a story of a lad."

His heart beat first, before bone grew and skin formed. His entire world a steady thump thump thump.

"He was a young lad. Younger than all of us gathered here. Between eighteen and twenty, if the stories can be believed. A clever boy, though."

Boots shifted against damp earth, hands dug deeper into pockets, searching for warmth. He was aware of all this, the movement, the bodies pressed together. The thrill, the nerves, the fear. He was of them, but apart from them.

"Now, the village is long gone. No one has lived there for over centuries. It was a simple place, nothing like the cities you all hale from. Where are you from, Sir?"

The woman's voice rang clear and sure, and the words had music to them. A practiced rhythm.

"Uh." A man, shaking with chill and awareness of twenty pairs of eyes on him. "Just outside London."

"London!"

"Er, yeah."

"Most of the villagers in these parts never left this area. Never saw London, were never a part of the hustle and bustle. Except the lad in our story. He was a doctor."

He couldn't see. Not yet. But he felt how the group moved in tighter, hands gripping each other harder.

"But he was an outsider. And the people in these parts didn't take to him right away. Close knit communities, you understand. They feared what was different, didn't trust his polish, his wealth."

His eyes opened, and blinked once. Twice. A full moon teased through the gaps in the trees, never quite giving enough light. He could make out impressions, shadows in the hollows of cheeks, the white of the storyteller's smile, the paleness of her hair.

"He was healthier than the villagers, stronger. Had an air of importance that they didn't take kindly to. At least, not at first."

Her words joined with the woods and stitched him together. From nothing to skin and blood and bone. To hair and breath and a sense of cold, sharp against this new body.

"Not until the sickness came. It decimated half of the county, killed many before the good doctor came up with a remedy. As you can imagine, the villagers were grateful. So grateful that they denied him nothing."

The mood shifted. Some in the group straightened, a perverse excitement replacing their boredom. Some leaned forward, others moved closer together. This was what they had come for. This was the meat of their tour.

"You've heard this part, I gather. It started small. He needed a vial of blood, a lock of hair. A bit of spit, a goat, a cow. The villagers gave him everything he asked for. He'd saved them, after all. Saved their children. How could they say no? What if he left? What if the sickness returned and there was no one to protect them?"

The woman grew solemn, and the woods responded. The winds died down, the shushing of the leaves disappeared.

"Nobody questioned his demands. There was no hesitation. Until he asked for a fresh human heart."

"No." The denial fell from his mouth. He hadn't done that. He'd never done that.

He thought they would turn to look at him, thought he would shock them out of this tale, but no. He went unheard.

"The villagers didn't want to risk his anger, but neither did they want to turn on each other." The woman spoke with more urgency. Tension grew and snapped tight. The people in the group – these *intruders* – were still, their eyes on the guide, all bated breath and rapt attention. "So, they went hunting."

He shook his head. That wasn't what had happened.

"It could be witchcraft, they mused. Perhaps he needed it for medical purposes. They didn't want to know. Every full moon, their doctor needed a human heart. So off they went, off to the next village. They murdered and stole, and returned full of triumph and the confidence that they were keeping their home safe."

She looked to the night sky.

"Tonight is a full moon. Imagine them, a group of men, the strongest and the bravest, move across here." She pointed east, drawing her finger west across the clearing. "Full of spirits and bravado."

Something snapped deep within the woods, loud enough to frighten the some of those gathered. A silent beat and then nervous laughs.

"No one could explain the killings. Not for many years. Until one night, they were seen. They were followed. Right to our doctor's doorstep."

His scalp prickled and he lost his newfound breath.

"He was chased him through these very woods, baying for his blood, for the death of the devil among them."

Figures appeared around the group, much like he himself had. They blinked into existence one after the other, made up of shadow and smoke, fury and violence.

"Our doctor ran for his life, but he wasn't fast enough. His screams tore through the night."

The new men took shape, their features sharpening, the eyes flashing. All watching him.

"They never found out what he was doing. That secret died with him."

He stumbled back as the figures closed around him.

"No. There is no secret," he said., his hands outstretched, pleading. "It's a lie. It's a show. There is no secret. It didn't happen. *You don't exist.*"

"As with all good ghost stories," the woman continued. "You can hear them if you listen carefully. Close your eyes, hold your breath, and listen for the Heart Eater in his last moments."

The mob she'd conjured grew closer, the details clearer, more solid, as her words gave them power. Their hands c urled into claws, their eyes empty, their teeth bared.

He turned and ran.

Susanna jerked and opened her eyes when she heard the scream. Babbling cries followed, rising in volume and desperation before they were abruptly cut off. Ed laughed next to her, his body shaking silently.

"I bet they've got speakers set up or something," he said, nudging her with his hip.

"Ha, yeah, probably."

Stupid to be so afraid. It was just a bit of fun.

SO DEADPOOL

KILLED THE

MARVEL UNIVERSE

SO DEADPOOL KILLED THE MARVEL UNIVERSE

JOSEPH S. PETE

The storyline played out cleverly, amusingly
with a sportive element of "how would he do that?"
before getting as meta as you'd imagine.
The super-powered Merc with the Mouth plowed through the assorted heroes,
and literary forebears like Don Quixote and the Headless Horseman,
bursting through the fourth wall
like the Kool-Aid Man with a subversive shtick.

Commodify Your Dissent, the Baffler said.
If I stopped dancing for my master, so can you, Deadpool told Omega Red
before showing him mercy in another narrative thread.

Deadpool does his jokey dog-and-chimichanga show,
killing off all the sacrosanct untouchables,
Spider-Man, The Avengers, all the pillars,
splattering radioactive spider brains on a city street,
tearing down the foundation, the whole canon.

Comics have a regenerative healing factor of their own.
Decimate a universe, wipe out a multiverse,
and just hit the reset button.
Every volume is a palimpsest
effacing everything that came before.

Deadpool killed off the whole Marvel universe
not just as promised in the title,
but after a beaucoup box office,
after every cosplayer at every Comic Con
donned the red and black,
the crossed swords and the dual guns.

But no one dies in comics.
The next movie gets everyone hyped
about some other character.
Canon gets rewritten.
The next issue erases all that came ere.

I WANTED TO TAKE YOU HOME BUT WHEN I DID IT WASN'T THERE

I WANTED TO TAKE YOU HOME BUT WHEN I DID IT WASN'T THERE

KIRSTY LOGAN

The first house I gave you was a tooth. The dentist pulled it to make space for the rest of my teeth, which apparently is often a problem for small-mouthed people when the wisdom teeth come in. He asked if I wanted the tooth, and I didn't particularly, but I also didn't want it to get thrown in the bin, so I wrapped it in a tissue and took it home. It was jagged at one end and it smelled sweet and a bit rotten. I got a nail from the toolbox and started to carve the tooth. I'll admit it wasn't worth putting in an art gallery, but by the end of the day my tooth was a tiny though recognisable house. I understand that when I presented it to you, half-joking, as we were brushing our teeth before bed, it was unexpected. You seemed pleased at the gesture, if a little disgusted. It wasn't your fault that the tooth got knocked into the toilet and accidentally flushed.

The second house I braided from my hair. There was a reasonable amount in my hairbrush, but not enough. I pulled out more from all over my head so that it wouldn't leave any obvious bald patches. My hair is long and thick so I managed two good handfuls without it looking much different, and its stiff curl meant it took to braiding well. The walls and roof were dense, and I even managed two windows. I shouldn't have surprised you by putting the hair next to your morning cup of coffee. As I was falling asleep the night before it had seemed quirky and charming, but I see now that it was a weird thing to do and made you not want to eat your scrambled eggs. It wasn't your fault that you left the hair on the roof of the car and then drove off. I like to think of it, this little perfect house I made – for you, from me – caught in a slipstream, tugged quick to the sky, blown off the motorway bridge to float down the river.

The third house was my fingernails. They made a beautiful roof, prettier than any tiles I've seen, each one painted a different colour. I realise that I only have ten nails so the roof was very small. It wasn't your fault that it somehow got put in the food scraps bin along with the onion skin and the carrot peels and the chicken bones.

That gave me an idea, and the next house was carved from the bone of my little finger. It was accidentally fed to the dog. My ear-house got buried in the window-box; my eye-house was squashed under your winter boots; my tongue-house was snatched by a neighbourhood fox.

I made you house after house after house. But each time it was too small, too loseable, too easily destroyed.

Finally, there I stand in front of you, everything removable or soft in me gone. I have made this final house for you: the rafters my ribs, the floor my flattened feet, the overheard light my unblinking eye. Come lie on the couch of the long bone of my thigh. Come rest your head on the cushion of my slow-beating heart. Come home.

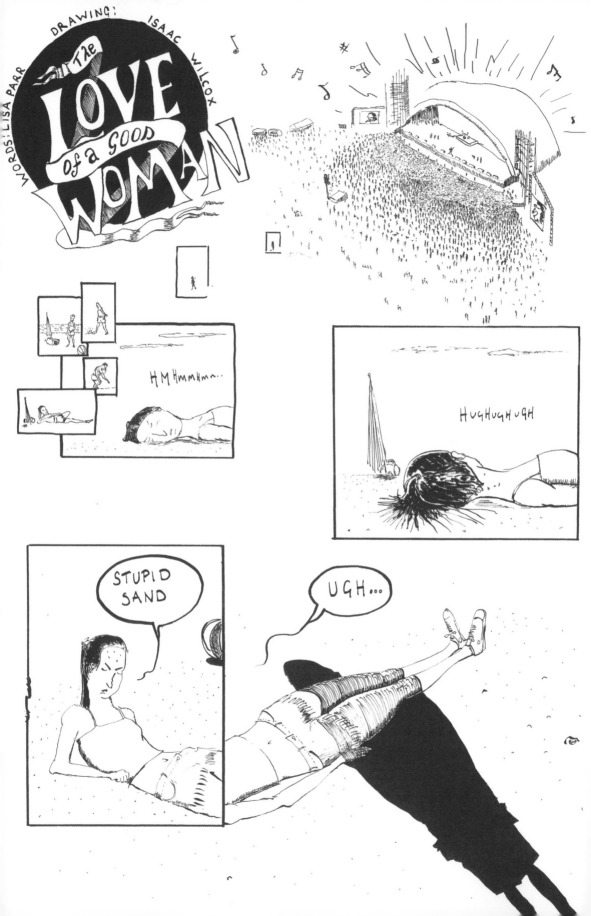

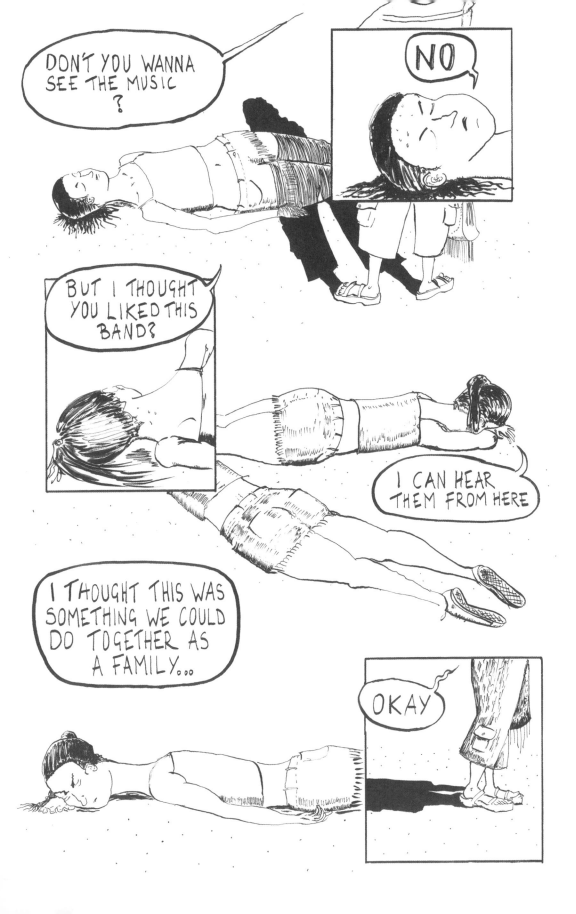

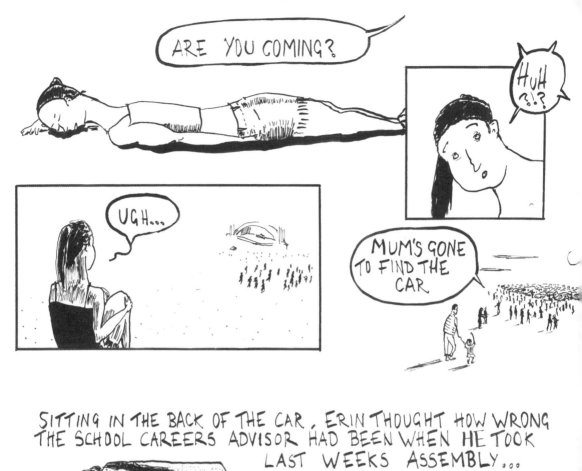

SITTING IN THE BACK OF THE CAR, ERIN THOUGHT HOW WRONG THE SCHOOL CAREERS ADVISOR HAD BEEN WHEN HE TOOK LAST WEEKS ASSEMBLY...

AND WARNED HER WHOLE YEAR...

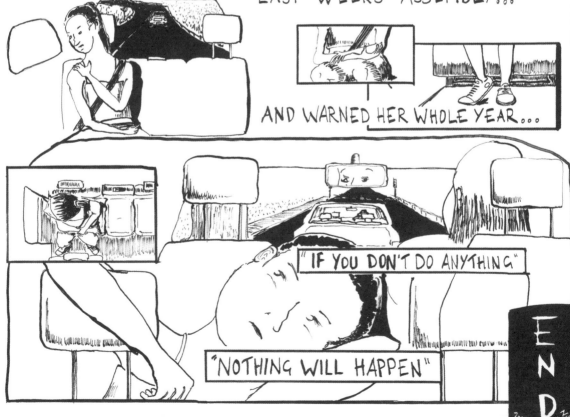

PAINTED STATIONS

PAINTED STATIONS
CALUM L MACLEÒID

His thumps find me groggy but seconds after the first rasping scrape I am at the door, spade in hand, listening. More thumps than scrapes; less damage to the door. As I try to swallow away the taste of nap the gap between thumps grows, as he tires.

"Shouldn't let me sleep like that, Chief," I grumble, bracing my shoulder to the door. Between thumps I force it, timed just sweet, the door's edge catching the man across the jaw. His knife clatters aside. He clasps his face. I lift the spade above my head.

#

This is my life. Every night, the man in the red jacket comes from the forest, attacks me with his hunting knife. Every night I kill him with my spade and bury him where the garden meets the forest. Morning comes and his grave is gone, as are any wounds he dealt me. That night, he comes from the forest again. Every night, over and over. For however long it's been. Feels like a fair while now.

#

"Late again Chief. Not good enough. Standards are slipping."

Some nights the clock-hands sweep round and round, my eyes droop as I wait for him. My muscles drag on my frame and I can't hold a thought to its end. Most days I deal with him long before he reaches the door. If not, he'll beat his fists against it for a while, but eventually he takes his knife to it. This ruins the paint and just creates more work for me the next day. Not that the man in the red jacket cares.

A good while back now, I realised the paint pots were not only replenishing themselves, but gradually altering the pigment of the paint itself. This helps me track the passage of time as well as revealing how deep he managed to get his blade. Sometimes I'll catch myself daydreaming, staring at the wrong rainbows he carves in it.

#

"He's a talkative one, isn't he? Right jabbermouth. Can't get a word in edge-ways!" I joke with Chief. The man in the red jacket never talks.

Chief was here before me. I recognise his smell in my dreams, and if I pay attention I can see his hand at work. Early on I realised I needed to talk, as I began to forget words and felt my thoughts losing their vigour. Our conversations also make it easier to cope with the fact of his presence. I am not certain if he is responsible for all of this, but he is certainly a key mover.

#

On a severe wooden chair, peering out the shed's single window into the gloom, I wait for him. Memories stumble around and settle on another chair. Not here, if that's possible. Windows too. Instead of looking out on the garden, it looked out at more windows. An office: a place and a role. A door people knocked. Staff. Clients. Interns. They would all knock my door politely. Memories are not to be trusted, but I am almost certain that none of them tried to gut me with a hunting knife.

Rust freckles all my metal, except the spade and the paint pots. There's a radio, but if any waves crease the aether, this device is not catching them. Beneath the bed, I store a large shard of mirror. When the mood takes me, I retrieve it and watch my decline. No matter how long I spend beneath the sun's glare, my skin remains the sickly white of seedling roots, marbled by seafoam green veins. These colours remind me of the garden. Mulch sweating. Chlorophyll stained knees.

#

Another garden too. I shouldn't dwell but there is little else for me to do. A day in that other garden. Running, chasing, but playing. I remember her. My wife, I think. She had a name. We all did. Our child too. My boy. Who's my boy? I used to ask him. Who's my boy? Where is he? I would coo. Where is he? There he is. There he is. I'm coming. Watch out. Here I come.

#

"This garden is getting to be a fulltime occupation Chief." Everything here grows ceaselessly, leaves and petals exploding from every limb and stem, and creepers crowd the shed. I leave them as long as I can bear before tearing, ripping, rending. Only the forest beyond the boundary never changes.

Finally, having mastered the territory, I bundle together the cuttings, dumping them all in a pile at the end of the garden. Usually I leave these to devolve into mulch. Sometimes I light bonfires.

My sleep is filled with fresh sap and airy blooms over the darkly sweet whiff of rot. Tumid stalks filling themselves in defiance and shoots grasping towards me.

Beyond the garden in every direction lies the forest. There is no point venturing there. I always get turned around and end up stumbling upon a stunningly familiar shed.

#

The garden makes me think of poems for some reason. About a book of poems I used to read them to him. One about a railway carriage. Fairy bread. My boy would drift off to sleep, borne there on the metre of each short verse.

#

"You ever think back to the early days Chief? When this was new? New to me anyway. You know, even after the first day, I think I understood. The second day, the day he returned, I waited in, staring at the door like a teenager staring at the phone. I used to think there was only the present. No back, no forwards but the scratches in the paint testify against that. I get it now though Chief. Don't I?"

#

One afternoon I'd had enough.

"I've had enough, Chief," I said, as the light began to fail. "This is it. This is the last one." I turned to address the mirror. I feel like I am looking Chief in the eye when I do that.

"Well, big guy," I said, wedging the door open with the spade, "it's been emotional. I can't pretend to understand, but I am ready. Whatever is next. It's in your hands Chief."

I bound my hands with my shirt and tugged it taught with clenched teeth and let the man in the red jacket come. He paused at the threshold, glowering down at me, then advanced. I closed my eyes and waited. All there was was the smell. He smelled of something bad, but comforting that I can't quite place. Then a slit of burning metal. Whistling. No breath. Progress.

The rays of colour that swim through the void slowly coalesced. I remembered that I am.

"Shit." When my vision settled, the image of the man in the red jacket lying face down with his skull caved in once again greeted me. The spade bloodied. I put my hand to my throat. Not a scratch.

"Shit." That was the night I smashed the mirror.

#

"Maybe this is your plan," I call out when painting the door. Cerulean. "You want me to keep painting this door. Layer upon layer. That's why I never run out of paint. And new colours too. Layer on layer on layer on layer. So many layers of paint on the door that it would bulge out, out into the garden, then a few million years later into the forests, then a couple of billion years out past the forest, until there is nothing but the painted door. That's it isn't it?"

Silence.

"You would tell me if I were right, wouldn't you?

#

You can't choke yourself with just your own hands. Your body won't let you. No matter how strong your resolve is, there always comes a point when that traitor, reptile part takes control, that part that only wants to keep on living forever, regardless of everything but the next breath, the next envoy through the system.

In this manner, there are some things that I am not permitted to remember. The details of what happened. Those days. That afternoon. Remembering is like wringing my own throat. Can't be done.

I remember the fact of his disappearance, but none of the details. Sometimes I panic, realising who I am and that I need to get out of here, that my family needs me. But there is only more forest beyond the forest, and a shed at the centre of it.

#

Who took him? Who took him from me? Who took him? Where is he now? Where is he? Where is my boy? What happened? He needs me. Where is he? Why is he not here with me where he belongs? When will I see him again? When will I smell him again? When will his impossible breath warm my neck?

#

After taking back control of the garden, I decide it has been too long since my last bonfire. I build one where the garden meets the forest. Fire can't touch the forest so there is no danger. The smoke is dark and thick. Bloom. Ablaze. Black. This gifts me an idea.

It screams and sizzles. Smoke as viscous as treacle squirts up from the flames as soon as the paint hits it. I empty both pots onto it. Charcoal tendrils weave their way away from the main stack. I inhale acrid symphonies, as I watch as the flames pat uselessly at the tree branches. Fire hypnotised, I don't notice the rain start.

And now the man in the red jacket is on fire, charging towards me from the flames. Now I too am on fire, but we are not fighting. We dance. In the rain. I swear. Not fighting. Two old enemies who, setting aside a pointless rivalry, realise they were colleagues all along. Ablaze, waltzing. Then he ruins it.

#

A dim dawn is seeping into the sky, by the time I am finished burying him. I collapse on top of the grave. Sunlight begins to gently toast the sweat off of my face. The sensation begs me to remember something. On the threshold of sleep, I remember another word: bath. Baths and another's body. Sleep draws me down and away from these fragilities before they can become anything more.

#

I wake to stars and mud. The shed door is closed. More than closed. Locked. He is in my house. Pressing my ear to the door I can hear him rooting around. Shifting my things. Making himself at home. Music plays. It's obscene. A light is on.

I beat the door and call down all of Chief's vengeance upon the usurping bastard's head. I scratch the paint until my nails break. I'm caught off guard when the door flies open, knocking me over. Now some woman is on top of me, beating me with a spade until I stop. I play dead. She buries me. There is no sign of the man in the red jacket.

#

When I awaken the next night, my muscles have healed and I am deep, deep within the forest.

At first, I tried to explain it to her. I politely rap the door. When there is no answer I begin to speak, apologising for the misunderstanding. Through the door I try to warn her about the man in the red jacket, and to explain the nature of Chief's existence and of the forest and that, most embarrassingly for all concerned, that she was actually in my house.

Her reply sounds loud. She does not speak a language I have ever heard. Garbled babbling. But the quivering in her voice would mean the same thing in any language.

"I'm sorry, I'm afraid I can't understand you."

Further barbarous mumbling.

"Slow down."

She does not.

"Look, we speak English here," I state. Open flies the door and my own spade crashes down upon me.

#

It takes only a few nights to perfect my creep. At the door, undetected, I run my hand over the scratch marks. I've gouged rainbow after rainbow into it but even their colours are fading. The paint smells of nothing.

"Why is she not painting it?" I whimper. "Chief, look. She's not even painting it."

I am still weeping against the door when she kicks it open and sends me sprawling yet again. There is something different about her. I can see her belly. It looks distended.

#

When I next awaken, foreign scents reach me. No dream remnants these, I realise as they refuse to clear, but instead grow in intensity as I make my way through the forest once again. Many smells that I do not recognise but there is one that I do, and it hangs over all the others. An unmistakable iron note. Blood. Human. Fresh.

"Is she dead, Chief? Did you kill her? You killed her, didn't you? You legend!"

Just in case I am mistaken, and this is all some trap, I skirt around to the window. Another smell. If the cold metal reality of blood had an opposite scent it would be this. It is warm and delicate, sweet and salty, buttery. Wholesome. And yet despite its obvious power, terrifyingly fragile. That's when I see the source. In her arms, a baby.

#

When the idea first grips me it is still shocking. A fading, redundant part of me knows that this is not normal behaviour, but the obvious facts of the matter soon silence that dissent. She is in my house. I am the one under attack, I am the wronged party, the displaced, the dispossessed.

She thinks she knows me. One night is all that it will take. One night she will make a mistake. Once I have the child she will know what to do. That we can trade. The child for the house. Simple.

I am waiting for her to make that mistake.

"Just one mistake Chief," I whisper with no mouth. "That's all it takes. All I need. Go on. Just give me one slip up. One misstep. Come on Chief, I'm ready. Let's do this. Come on. I'm ready and I'm here. I'm fucking here..."

FRANKENSTEIN
WAS A MONSTER

FRANKENSTEIN WAS A MONSTER

SIOBHAN DUNLOP

He dreams of the freedom his creator never gave him.

Electrical current spikes through his veins.
If only he could electrocute.

What a fucking bastard, he'd say, but he can't.
His English comes from Milton. What a Satan,
What an Eve, what an Adam. What a God.

Even his pronouns are not his. It. He,
Made from pieces of men, but not a man,
A monster. Frankenstein's monster. Owned by another,
Stealing scraps of knowledge in an alpine retreat,
He wishes for the power to live like any other.

He who was forced into being cannot simply be.
Revenge he learns from humanity, not from within himself.
This revenge will make him human.

He learns how to reject rationality, for it is
A luxury he is not allowed to have.
Brutal force. Black lead in secondhand arteries.

He is what people see him as, now.

Frankenstein was the man, not the monster.
Some don't see it that way.

PLAYING
VIDEO GAMES

PLAYING VIDEO GAMES:

Sex in space, trans missions and real-life superpowers

GARY MARSHALL

If you have ever played video games you'll be familiar with the power-up, the reward you get for succeeding in an element of the game. In an outer world shooting game you might start off with a slow ship, with guns not much better than pea-shooters to take on enemies. With each power-up gained your guns get better, your shields stronger, your spaceship faster.

If you're LGBT, there are power-ups in the real world too.

Being out, in even a small way, is a power-up. LGBT people are often quite vulnerable. We've had years of being told we either don't exist or that there's something deeply wrong with us and, while, legislatively, Scotland's just dandy for LGBT people, we're well aware that to many people we're still considered abominations or potential victims. If and when we take our tentative first steps into the world, our powers are far from fabulous. We're expecting to be verbally abused at best, maybe physically attacked at worst.

Every small victory a power-up. Come out to your best friend and get a hug? Power up! Get a surprisingly loving response from a parent? Power up! Go to Pride? Power up! Commit daring acts of cross-gender dressing by wearing very slightly skinnier jeans than usual? Power UP!

But the role of video games isn't just a metaphor. The escapism they offer is particularly valuable for LGBT people who want to lock the doors and inhabit a different world for a while. And if you're trans, some of them enable you to play as the gender you feel you should be, not the one you've been assigned.

Every bit of acceptance, no matter how grudging or qualified, makes you that little bit stronger. You walk a little taller, a little prouder, a little more confident. And as the power-ups accumulate, you begin to discover that the things you fear aren't so scary any more. In my own case, coming out as trans to a national radio audience and bouncing around the city centre as a baldy old man in a skirt has done wonders for my shyness, social anxiety and fear of being judged by others.

For many trans people one of the first explorations into alternative gender options and into being who you truly are were through MMORPGs, massively multiplayer online role-playing games. Many of those games enabled you to play as all kinds of characters, human and non-human, hobbits, space aliens and creatures from other dimensions. As many trans people discovered, when you communicate with other players in an MMORPG they're quite happy to keep everything in character, so if your character is female you'll be addressed as such. That isn't always a good thing – there's plenty of misogyny online, and online games aren't immune to that – but to be recognised as and treated as the gender you feel, even if only on a computer screen, is astonishingly empowering.

I never really got into MMORPGs, but I fell hard for a sci-fi series called Mass Effect. In the first three Mass Effect games you play Commander Shepard, and that commander can be John or Jane. Not only is Jane Shepard better company – she's voiced by the wonderful Jennifer Hale, who makes even the daftest dialogue breathe – but you can completely customise the character's appearance in the game. Hair colour, facial structure, eye shape, jawline, hair, makeup… given enough time (and believe me I gave myself enough time), you could create a Jane Shepard who was an idealised version of your feminine self.

It was enormously exciting. I – Jane – went around the universe kicking alien ass while also rocking some pretty great daytime looks. It wasn't the only game where I could play as a female character, but in Jane Shepard I was able to create an avatar that looked like the person I really wanted to be, not a cookie-cutter female shape with improbably curves in a space helmet you couldn't see into. Playing Shepard felt strange. Playing Shepard felt good. Playing Shepard made the game matter so much more than if I'd been playing the archetypal Space Marine Fighting Space Monsters In Space.

Oh, and the game also let your character have sex – and not just the usual straight man/woman binary, but across genders and species. It caused a great deal of controversy at the time, because while gamers had no problem with interspecies alliances (the same man with sexy-space-chick trope that goes back to Star Trek), same-sex attraction couldn't possibly be a thing in the far future. There was a similarly childish response to the more recent Horizon: Zero Dawn, where boys threw tantrums when they discovered the protagonist was female, fully clothed and didn't have improbably large breasts.

The romantic options in Mass Effect added extra depth to what was really a soap opera with space battles, but unfortunately just like in real life you can't always be with the person you want to be with. The relationship I wanted to explore, Jane with sassy fellow traveller Miranda Lawson, wasn't an option in the game. I clearly wasn't the only person disappointed: the internet is packed with fan fiction where Jane and Miranda get to do what the game's writers denied them.

As games get more realistic and immersive, the ability to inhabit the gender and character you want, that's going to become even more powerful. Imagine how it would feel to play in virtual reality as the female character you maybe wanted to be, experiencing the world through her eyes and experiences.

It turns out that for some trans people, video games aren't escapism at all. They help us discover and explore who we really are.

While fighting space monsters.
In space.

OUR DAYS
OF YOUTH

OUR DAYS OF YOUTH

MATTHEW MEYER

I saw the sky tear for the first time in two thousand years. The once perfect blue sphere that had stood unscathed after thousands of battles was now showing it could not handle the stress any longer. The robot lord Ceperous was winning the new battle.

It wouldn't be long before Ceperous' army would be flying through the tear in the sky. My group of four Super Soldiers had fought the army on more than one occasion, and the latter battle was one we had thought was the final stage. We had developed a portal that transferred Ceperous and his army into a dimension where escape should have been impossible. Now, here he was, ripping a hole in the sky where, really, he was ripping a hole in the other-worldly dimension.

My soldiers and I braced ourselves on top of the Kronous, our flying headquarters. Down below us, the rest of the world grew in a parade of increasing panic. Even from well above a thousand feet from the tallest skyscraper, we could hear horns blaring and vehicles crashing into each other. They were not sounds we haven't heard before, but they were thunderous against our eardrums, making our hearts race and filling our veins with an adrenaline that kept us going. Ever since our adventure of curiosity, many years ago, we had made a pledge that we would not let this world of ours be submitted to a bunch of alien scum.

It had all seemed like it was yesterday. We were just a group of four ordinary children. We got up for school just like every other kid, ate breakfast, showered, and grumbled our way down the four blocks to the Salom Junior High School. We all had one class together, algebra, and we were not looking forward to it because of a test that counted for thirty percent of our grade.

We suffered through the classes, almost fell asleep in study hall, and were excited to get home because it was Friday, and Friday night meant group movie night.

It was Roger's idea to make a detour to the local plant. It was a facility that produced trailers. His uncle had worked the second shift, and Roger wanted to deliver a message before he started the shift. Huge clumps of thick, black smoke puffed out of three smoke stakes continuously for six days straight, and lay dormant on Sunday when the three shifts were off. They had heard of a special department within the facility that just handled the chemical waste water that was left over after the steel was manufactured. Clean water was supposed to flow through a tube down a small creek when the waste water was diluted with some special chemical to make it environmentally friendly. Someone must not have been paying attention that one fateful day, because when Roger wanted to go sticking his nose around the back of the facility, he stumbled upon some of that chemical water flowing down the creek.

"I don't think the water's supposed to look like this!" He said. "It's *glowing!*"

Sure enough, it was. My logic was that the sunlight was bouncing off it. For some strange, other-worldly reason that to this day we still don't know for sure, each of the four of us had the urge to stick our fingers into the glowing, orange goo.

At first, everything was normal. Roger got his message delivered, and we would go our separate ways until eight o'clock when movie night started. It was then that our lives would change forever.

We were comfortable on the couch, until we felt like we had a sudden attack of the flu. I was instantly overcome with nausea. The strong feeling of vomiting was all I could think about, but surprisingly, no one did. The room spun, and we all ended up on the floor. I had a vague sense of my surroundings, and no idea of who I was.

Then, the nausea seemed to melt away and in its place was a powerful force that surged through my body. The only way it could be described was like being in an electric chair minus the pain. My body shook and I could feel my muscles and limbs grow. I believed my heart raced faster than that of a race horse. After it was all over I should have been at least ten feet tall, but I wasn't. None of us were. At first, we all looked like the same fourteen-year-old kids with snarky attitudes. The only evidence from our little episode was the beating of my heart, which was still racing faster than a race horse's.

We all looked at each other, speechless for about a minute. Then Emily finally spoke up. "What the Hell was that?!"

I shrugged. "You got me!"

"Is everyone okay?" Jessica asked.

"I guess so…" Roger stammered. He was the only who still appeared shaken up, however, he was also known to be somewhat of a hypochondriac.

"If everyone's fine," I said, "then how about we just keep this little incident to ourselves?"

They all agreed, and for the next two days we tried to erase the incident entirely. It was then that the true nature of the incident was starting.

Emily was first one to notice that she could turn invisible. The guy she had a big crush on had finally spoke to her, asking if she knew what movie was playing at our local theatre. She was so nervous she stuttered, and barely managed to get the title of the movie out. The guy just formed half of a smile and said thank you. Emily was so frustrated and embarrassed she wished she could hide away from everyone-and she got her wish.

Somehow, as she was going off at the mouth, her whole body vanished. We all stared at her in open mouthed bewilderment, just listening to a voice. It was me who finally said, "Emily! You've *disappeared!*"

That night, we all sat in my parent's basement, pondering how Emily got this extraordinary power. It was more or less just the three of us, because Emily kept playing the, Now-You-See-Me, Now-You-Don't game.

We eventually all came to the conclusion that it had to be the result of the chemical water we had touched. We began figuring out what else we could do. Roger was the next one to discover he could shoot out fire from his hands. His whole arm was like a powerful flame-thrower. Next was Jessica, and her ability to emanate electricity from her body. For me, it was super strength. I could pick up objects that weighed tons, destroy buildings with one punch, run faster than a bullet, and jump higher than the tallest building in the world.

It was agreed among us that we needed to keep our powers to ourselves. If the world knew there were actual superhero-like kids walking around, they would either lock us away or study us like we were aliens, or they would expect us to be saviours. It was too much for four children to handle, so for the next two years we kept it under wraps, until we discovered something else extraordinary.

None of us had aged. We hadn't grown. Our skin had not grown any more distinct than it was. The pimples on Roger's face hadn't disappeared, even with the skin care products. Even Emily had cut her hair and realized it wasn't growing. We weren't changing at all.

After this observation, it was unanimously decided that we couldn't lead a normal life, at least not at that point. We couldn't go back to school, we couldn't go to the movies; we couldn't be a regular kid. If everyone noticed that we weren't growing older, what would they do? Our parents put out Amber Alerts for us for two years before I guess giving up. It broke our hearts, but this was the way it had to be.

For a long while we all hated our new powers by then, and tried to find out ways to reverse the effects. We went back to the plant, we tried researching it on the internet, but we couldn't find anything related to actual real-life super-powers. We even considered the possibility of revealing ourselves.

We didn't reveal ourselves until the first legitimate attack on our city. Another three years had passed, and during that time we had no choice but to accept the fact that we were different and that this was our lives. When we were attacked by some slimy, snake-like creature with no brains whatsoever, it seemed evident that this was no fairy-tale. There *were* evil aliens out there around us, and that strange and unnatural things *do* occur, and that it must be our destiny to protect the world.

It took some days for the rest of the world to accept us as still children of Earth but also as defenders of the human race. Our parents didn't care. They were shocked, yes, but mostly overjoyed that we weren't dead. When our parents and the rest of the world accepted our new fates, it was then that we started to have a new respect for our abilities. We fought as a team, and kicked some ass. It was only then that our superpowers felt awesome.

Over time, with our minds still young and sharp, we developed new technologies that we used not only to our advantage but for everybody else. It was inevitable, because the attacks became more frequent and more challenging. They were no longer slimy, snake-like creatures with no brains, but more inferior and dangerous creatures that controlled armies, like our new friend Ceperous.

"We're gonna have to find a clear landing!" I shouted over our microphones built into our custom-made ship helmets. "See if you can blast those drones, Roger!"

"Roger that!" He answered, then I heard a little giggle in the background.

We flew our mini-ship off Kronous and, dodging swarms of Ceperous' robot attackers, finally were able to ignite an escape hatch to land on the top of Ceperous enormous mothership.

Ceperous was a gigantic robot, but his brain was an actual alien brain. He shot missiles from his arms, had a rocket launcher from his back, and commanded an entire army just by telepathy, for he did not speak. As soon as we landed, Ceperous' army charged at us, blocking our path to the robotic overlord.

"Get ready for battle, guys!" I announced.

At this stage in our lives, we were used to this. Emily disappeared and started taking out the army by surprise. One punch from me sent the robots sailing off the mothership. Roger incinerated about twenty of them, and a shot of five-hundred degree electrical current from Jessica got the rest.

"Take that, you alien scumbags!" She shouted.

"You picked the wrong day to mess with us!" Emily exclaimed.

I shouted to the group as five missiles shot through the air. We dodged them, but the explosion left us a bit shaken. Ceperous fired again, and then shot off a rocket that shook the entire ship. Roger shot out his flames, Jessica let out a burst of electricity, and I pounded the floor with both of my fists.

"He's not *that* smart of an alien!" Jessica said. "He's destroying his own ship!"

Eventually, the mothership began to falter, mainly because Ceperous was reaching defeat. His mechanical suit was buzzing and sparking, and it looked like we had the opportunity to finally put an end to his reign of terror. However, the floor beneath him began to open up, and before any of us could react, he disappeared beneath the ship.

"We have to get off the ship!" I shouted. I summoned our mini-ship by pushing some buttons on my custom-made battle suit. We all hop on just as the mothership was charging to blast off into the slit in the sky. We landed back safely on Kronous, and we all witnessed Ceperous and his army retreating to their dimension.

"We did it!" Roger exclaimed, slapping everyone on the back.

"Yeah, but only for now!" I said. "He'll be back!"

There are some days that I wish we were still normal, especially when I observe my classmates carrying out normal day-to-day lives. They have families of their own, and although that might seem to be the boring life compared to ours, I still would give up a piece of it just to experience what it would feel like. I pretty much speak for everyone, except Roger, who is happy that girls at least *talk* to him despite his acne.

There is no routine for when the planet gets attack, and not all villains are the same. We are on call, no matter how much we hate it. There are many nights when we're in the middle of a movie or video game, and the built-in sensors we had installed on our watches signal that the world is yet again in jeopardy. We never have any time to brace ourselves to prepare for what's to come. So far, Ceperous is most superior in intellect as any alien yet to surface, but it seems that his attacks grow more devious every time.

Whether we like it or not, this is our lives. We haven't met an alien we couldn't defeat, and as long as we're alive, there won't be. Despite what others might say, we are not invincible, but we damn near feel like it sometimes. They say teenagers think they're indestructible, but we're wise enough to know better. The world needs us, and we wouldn't change it *for* the world.

CONFEDERATE STATUES

CONFEDERATE STATUES

MELISSA CARMACK GOODBOURN

i.

Take them down! Take them down!

I need no reminder and let's not call this history, your bigotry lives and breathes. It runs
through the South like veins, like the Mississippi. It is so much a part of this place and I've heard it
all my life in some form or another, in two words or a nod, in a car-door-locked driving through
a different neighbourhood. We always used to say:
        'He's from another generation'
but now you're my generation, my daughter's generation and there you stand lighting the street
with tikki torches meant for back decks and barbeques, moonlit nights and mosquitoes, but no,
instead you decide you'd like to own something else.

I do not know why I am surprised. Before
I called you uneducated. I called you ignorant. I said,
        'You only learnt what you were taught' but I have no compassion left,
for you.

So take them down, take them down!

We need no confederate hero for you to hang your hats on. No more excuses to shout
        'For our continued existence of the white race…'
They say you are scared because you know you are losing! It is not your fear I want. I want regret

and humility, openness and transparency, re-districting and democracy, the ability to understand power can be shared, like love

I want justice.

For each corner of the world to know *My South* – the one where you can walk down the street
where you know all your neighbours and at Christmas they bring ham, pick-up your drunk uncle and bring him back in, where they drop-off fresh tomatoes so everyone is fed. Where no one has patience for a sugar-spooned mouth and gentlemen do not confuse hate speech with freedom. Where people stand together in democratic spaces, in church halls over coffee, in polling places, and drive slowly down gravel roads without feeling afraid of the cops or condemned by white 'Christians'.

But I doubt now that place ever existed. And here we are – me raging and you marching, unable to listen, to understand what it means to be

human.

ii.

Take them down, take them down –

from my Facebook feed, my Senate and my Congress! Expel them from our universities, from our college campuses! And for God's sake, impeach them from my White House!

Robert E. Lee may have been a general but he was also a bigot. There was courage on both sides and
I know those grey boys lost more than just the war but it doesn't mean what they fought for was worth it. Poverty still clings to their kin, but it doesn't make it right when there's not a single mention of the black women and men who died, heroines and heroes, who nursed the soldiers' wounds and spied for the Union, and who still worked the cotton. No, I've never seen a statue
of John Langston, of Harriet Tubman, and it's the same mouths protesting her face on the $20 dollar bill who say
          'We should remember our heritage!'

So you cannot convince me, these statues tell the whole story. Or the right story.

iii.

It's time to stop pretending we don't see colour.

According to the numbers we see it when we're hiring, when we're reading CVs.
We see it in the footage of another black boy beaten by community police. And
it's time to stop worrying
about politically correct protests. Not everything can be fixed by re-naming our
highways
after Martin Luther King Jr. We need to acknowledge that for some of us it is
easier
to walk down the street, to apply for college or a visa, to be released on bail or
never charged
to begin with – that for some of us our paths were already greased (with money,
a white face or a dick.)

Let's not argue semantics. Instead, let's hear each story

even when it's recriminating.

Let's lace our shoes in protest

when friends and even family are on the other side.*

I've heard all your excuses and I'm ashamed

to admit, I've used them. But it's time to draw a line.

When they plow through us

if we're standing in the millions they cannot win.

iv.

My Dad says, 'When I hear cicadas singing, I know it is spring.' If we all call
out together
we can change this season too.

Start with a whisper.

                              Take them down, take them down.

Say it from your stomach.

                         Take them down, Take them down.

Roar until it echoes!

                         Take them down, Take them down!

until a wall of protest drowns out the 'us' and 'them,'
until we call them terrorists and hold them to account
until we stand so many, they cannot tell whose voice is shouting from which
mouth.

Then these relics will be dragged away.
(*And for each empty shoe left on the street, we will pick it up and all walk home
together.)

YER DA'

DARREN HEPBURN

It was Wednesday night and Gerry had just finished his last shift at work before a well-earned fortnight off. He was just about to pull into his drive when he noticed his phone light up in a wee compartment next to his gear stick. It was his mum, Marge. His mum never phoned so something must have been up. He answered and right away he wished he hadn't. She was in hysterics and pleaded with him for help. He could barely understand a word she was saying. "Maw calm doon, what's wrang?"

"Gerry just come hame. It's yer da. I'm scared."

"What? What's he done?"

"Just come hame." She hung up.

'Fuck', Gerry thought. He knew he was gonnae have to pop round which was a nightmare because he really hated dealing with his mum and dad fighting. They used to fight a lot when he was younger and he'd always managed to hide away in his room and avoid getting caught up in it all. But there was no avoiding it this time. He'd been requested.

It wasn't too long before he arrived and when he pulled into his parents drive, he saw immediately what was going on. His dad was in the garden. He was bollock naked – bar a bath towel he'd tied round his neck like a cape. Gerry watched as his dad ran in circles around the garden. His cape flapping in the wind. One arm outstretched. His cock bouncing about slapping against his thighs with every step.

He knew, just by watching him from his car window that this was going to last all night. He considered phoning his wife and letting her know he'd be late. He didn't. He just let out a big sigh, and went away to get his dad back in the house.

First he tried to get in front of his dad and stop him from running. But his dad just swerved out the way and laughed. To be be honest, his dad had never looked happier. It was comforting to see him like that. Blissfully unaware that his wife was in the house crying or that the kids across the road were filming him and sending snapchats to their mates.

"Gerry did ye see me there?"

"Aye da I saw ye. How about we get ye in and get ye some troosers or some-thing on ye?" Gerry wondered if maybe is dad had started showing signs of dementia. He was definitely getting old enough for it. But his memory was as sharp as ever. Gerry was still trying to get in front of his dad but he kept swerving out the way.

"Da, fuckin stop." His dad started laughing and bolted away down the street. His left arm still outstretched.

Seconds later, out came Marge still in tears. "Gerry! He hasnae stopped for hours. He thinks he can fly and he's been running aboot since lunchtime." She looked a mess. Gerry asked her to explain what was going on.

"I've come out the shower and clocked him watching Superman 2. He tells me he reckons he could fly. Says it's a piece of piss."

Gerry put his hand on Marge's shoulders. "I telt him to stop being daft. I thought he was kidding on but he just chucked the table at me and flew away."

The wee wooden table was upturned on the floor. Fag ash and cans of lager were strewn across the living room. Gerry smiled. He thought this might have been a wind up. A joke or something. But it wasn't. No this was real. His dad thought he was Superman.

His mum collapsed onto the couch. "I just dinnae ken how to help him. He's out there telling folk he can fly. Running about in circles. What am I gonnae dae?" Gerry promised her he'd get him back home. He lived for this kind of carry on. Just weirdos being let loose on society. Now here he was, finding out his dad was one of them. It was brilliant.

He left the house and started to walk down the street. Looking left then right, up the various streets and alleyways for his auld man. Eventually he got to the park at the end of the road. It was just a wee park with a set of swings and a slide. Hardly anyone used it, but sure enough there was his dad in a park trying to explain to a little boy that he was gonnae fly away.

"I can fly, I just need to get the speed," Gerry heard him say to the boy before the boy bolted into a nearby house. "Da," he shouted "come home, this is daft." His dad looked at him, waved and then flew away. Gerry knew he was going to have to chase after him. But his auld man was too quick. Far too quick.

The two of them were running through a wooded area that the local young team used for racing bikes. There wasn't a real path but there was smoothed out dirt for walking along. It was tough ground to run on. Gerry's dad still had one arm out in front of him and he'd even started making whooshing sounds as he weaved in and out of invisible trees.

"Stop, I just want tae talk!" Gerry shouted. He was starting to get tired. They'd only been running for a few minutes but Gerry never had the stamina for running. He couldnae believe his dad who'd been running non-stop since lunchtime was still so full of energy. Maybe he was a superhero. "I'll never stop. I'm about tae fly."

His dad looked back to see his son. His offspring. His own blood, chasing after him, trying to stop him from living his dream.

Rage flooded through Gerry's dad. He couldn't believe for a second that his own son could be trying prevent him from the wonder of human flight. This was everything he'd been wanting since he was little. He remembered when he was just a lad and him and all his mates used to play flying in his back garden. They'd fly about shooting lasers at each before dinner was ready. Hours wasted just playing with no objective. Why would his own son want to take that away from him?

Gerry was within touching distance of his father. He was almost able to reach out and grab him but then something happened. Gerry's dad threw one of his arms behind him and started shooting.

"Pew pew pew." He was making laser sounds. Just like when he was wee. Just like during the games he'd played as a youngster. Except this time it was working.

The force that came from the blast was enough to knock Gerry backwards and onto the ground. He was stunned. Physically stunned by the blast but also mentally stunned by the fact that his dad had just shot him with magic lasers that came from his fingers.

Meanwhile, his dad continued running. Until he wasn't running anymore. His feet lifted from the ground and he took off. Gerry watched from the dirt as his dad flew away into the sky. His cape made him look heroic as he glided across the sky. Gerry squinted. He could still see his dad's cock.

PICTURING PATTI SMITH

REBECCA MONKS

1.

He never thought a photograph could be art.

You tell the policeman that when he asks why you did it, but he doesn't write it down.

'Anything else?'

He's shaking his foot against the table. You watch the water in his drinking glass ripple in agreement with the disturbance.

You clear your throat.

'As far as I'm concerned, being any gender is a drag,' you say, in your best affected accent.

'What?'

His question is a dare. You lean in and steady the table. He stops shaking his foot and furrows a brow at you, heavy with slick, grey hairs.

'Patti Smith said that,' you say. 'And I agree.'

You lean back, hoping you have risen to his challenge.

Authority is his, no matter what Patti says.

2.

He never thought a photograph could be art.

'It's just pointing and clicking,' he says, sitting too close to you now.

You study the lines on your father's face: tokens purchased with sleepless nights and easy lager. The way his lip curls when he's begging you to take the bait. The way his face reminds you of your own when it's stubborn and shining.

He hands you a pile of prints. You see these moments as though they have been carved in marble, filled with paperwhite smiles.

You used to sacrifice your smile to that camera as though it were a God.

'I took most of these ones didn't I?' he's saying, rubbing the corner of his eye with a flaking thumb. You do that when you're drunk, too. 'Reckon I'm an artist like you, Hannah Banana?'

You want to tell him that he could be if he wanted to, but you don't. Instead, you take the bundle and push the corners together, straightening the pile in your hands. Your thumb brushes over a picture of him, years younger and shades lighter. He winces.

'Don't get your grubby fingers on them! These are the only copies I've got!'

You cough an apology and straighten up, taking care to only touch the edges from now on. Your fingers dance around corners.

You tell him that you like them, but he knows that you don't. He never let you hold the camera when you were young.

Someone on the television show you were half-watching screams. He doesn't seem to hear it. Sometimes you wonder if he's just staring at the box, which burns on into the night, never taking in a thing.

'Some good times there girl,' he says, shifting closer to you. His leg is still too close to yours. His breath is sour and hot. 'Some good times we've had.'

There's the two of you in Spain. You, spinning wildly in the pool; him, reading

John Grisham beside it. Who captured this blurry memory you wonder, if not the two of you?

There you are in Spain again - a different part of Spain of course - and you're grinning with a cocktail umbrella behind your ear. What were you then - eleven? Twelve?

There are no pictures of this house, you notice. There are no pictures of your mother from back then. No. He only takes pictures far away from home, where with enough cheap cerveza, he could be happy to have a daughter like you.

There's the two of you in Majorca.

Maybe you were fifteen?

Maybe.

You put the pictures on the table, and he glows. His point is made.

'See what I mean Banana?' he says, leaning back on the sofa. His knee knocks into yours. 'You should listen to me. Anyone can be a photographer. How much are they asking for that course?'

You say it's a little over nine thousand and he scoffs.

'You should spend that money on something real,' he says, turning back around to face the television. 'No daughter of mine is going to be a poncey photographer.'

The prints go back into the box. You know he'll never give you the money.

3.

When you shut the door behind you, you breathe out. That pain gone from your chest. Those pins and needles laying off.

You're happy to be away from your street, with its cobbles and used needles and neighbours. The women trying to be your mother now you don't have one anymore. The men wondering what you'll look like when you're older, and if they'll be that much older too.

Your street is all red brick and net curtains. You pass a corner shop with yellow cardboard for windows. You watch as they queue, turning their dole money into brown liquor. You pass a field where shrubs and weeds grow around empty coca cola cans. The air is thick with the smell of nothing.

The bus takes you into the town. You pass tourists in tartan, desperate to decorate their body in what they think is the uniform of a country. You want to tell them it isolates them, but instead you just stare out of the window, watching the shapes the world makes when it's moving.

You head into the National Gallery and thumb through the catalogue. There's a newer one online, but it's nice to hold something in your hands.

You see the sheep in formaldehyde and wonder how it still looks so soft. You think of your mother bathing you and wrapping you in a towel, and wonder if she'd ever been here.

You see Peploe's painting of rocks on Barra, and think how ordinary it is.

You see the Lichtenstein, and think how ugly it is.

Then you see her: Patti Smith.

Patti Smith.

Your mother loved her, and so did you. Two women in formaldehyde, listening to spinning disks.

That night all those years ago, 'People Have the Power' was playing in the background. You can't listen to that song now.

As you watched from the bottom of the stairs, from behind crisscrossed fingers, he pleaded his case.

He told her those women meant nothing, but she laughed and said 'I mean something,' and you remember nodding in agreement even though she couldn't see you. Even though she didn't know you were there.

You wonder why she didn't take you with her when she left. You wonder if she'd have paid for the course. You wonder if she still loves Patti Smith.

You study the photograph again. Light peaks through windows and frames her naked body. She is crouched and she is beautiful. You've always loved black and white.

Patti Smith looks beautiful in black and white.

You realise you'll never take a photograph this beautiful as long as he lives. You want to see art in people the way that others do. You want more than a handful of prints. You want angles and lines and to capture a moment in life so rare that it will last forever.

Patti Smith looks so beautiful in black and white.

Patti Smith was brave, you think. Patti Smith did what she wanted, you think.

Patti Smith just looks so beautiful in black and white.

You take the blade from your bag as carefully as you can.

You whisper an apology, and drag the edge across every inch of the thing you have stared at for weeks.

The paper peels and hangs. Patti's images blisters and shreds. Somewhere an alarm sounds.

The photograph clings to the wall as if to cling onto life.

You slip the knife back into the bag, and think of your mother.

It's ruined, you think, and you smile.

4.

He never thought a photograph could be art.

You tell the policeman that, when he asks why you did it.

I, A POET, DO NOT, LIKE STORIES

I, A POET, DO NOT LIKE TORIES

ANDREW BLAIR

I, a poet, do not like Tories
Yet still they come;
Sputtering forth their truculent seed
Across comfortable, fed bellies.
I, a poet, do not like Tories
And I inform people why
At every available opportunity,
Yet still they multiply.
Carcass after carcass after carcass.
Yet still they multiply.

I, a poet, do not like Tories.
Do any poets like the Tories?
I know lots of poets, far more than I know Tories.
There's anywhere between five
and five hundred people who now know
I,
a poet,
do not like the Tories
Yet,

Somehow
They persist;
Their insistence on taking nice things
And breaking them
Is more popular than poetry
Will ever be.

I, a poet, do not like Tories.
You, a poetry audience,
do not like Tories.

Well,
At least there's that.

At least there's that.

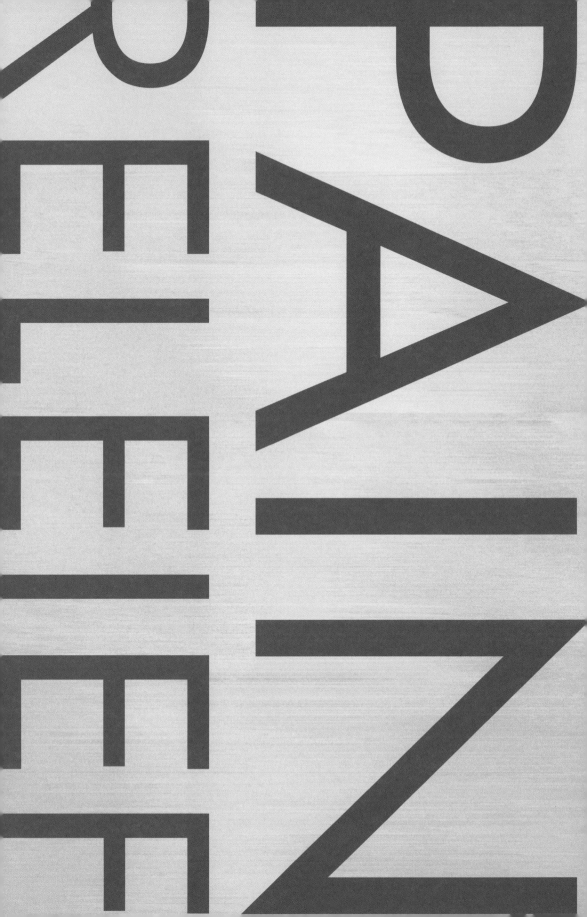

PAIN RELIEF

CAROLINE GREBBELL

The man sits.

He looks to the object resting in his palm. He tears along its edge, letting the shrink foil drop to the floor at this feet before raising his hand. He feels the steely callous fused to the bone of his skull. His fingertips tingle against its dissolute boundaries as he slides the flash drive into the port and closes his eyes.

The sun is high. It appears to be fiercely hot. A breeze disturbs the limbs of a willow. It scatters shadow as seed across a schoolgirl as she moves through the grass towards the pond. She stops and turns, her face plunged into darkness. Sunlight bleeds through the edges of untidy hair. She leans over, the hem of her pink cotton dress rising at the back as she parts the grass beneath her. Behind her a ragged line of crows stare, hunched over, into shallow waters.

He watches her. His breath is thin and inconsistent. His hands are wet.

'I found one!' The girl drops to her knees. 'Parnassia palustris! I found one!' She signals. 'Tilly! Tilly! Come and see.'

A second girl appears. Her legs are longer, her dress shorter. She lowers herself to sit. Crosslegged, her knees fall apart, the fabric of her dress dipping between.

Suddenly a face. It is close and smiling.

'I love your hat Mrs Bingham.'

A hand comes into view at the bottom of frame. The liver spotted skin of an older woman, fingers softly curved.

His arm is outstretched, fingers awkward and bent.

A crow drags a frog from the water. It tears at the tensile flesh then glances back towards the viewer as a rigid claw pins flailing legs in place. The woman's hand reaches out towards the schoolgirl's face, the downy line of her jaw. The eyes blink slowly and connect with those of the viewer. The eyes are blue.

'You really are becoming quite a beauty Susan.' The woman's hand touches the girl's face.

He leans forward, the power pricking and flicking in his groin. The rounded flesh of the plump cheek, soft and moist with sweat. A pulse of pressure at the base of his spine. His heart is beating hard. He pulls the flash drive from his skull and his head falls forward and sweat drips from his brow. His eyes settle on the fine line of black text.

Recall-D446/2:K-Psychi © *· TRACKED against unauthorised activation.*

RE: ENQUIRY

---

donotreply <KnoweCare.@info.net>

Dear Mr. Bingham

I must confirm that I am not in the position to grant you access to our records.

Exicco patches relieve the pain of osteoporosis and are extremely efficient. Their application and renewal is carried out by fully trained KlevoPsychi professionals.

Your wife is Stage 4: CDR-2 so will exhibit erratic powers of recall, a symptom of dementia and one which will not improve. This is very upsetting to all of us as Nancy is a big part of the community at Leafy Kno we but if you are experiencing increased distress, there are several excellent dementia support groups in your area.

I would also kindly ask you to cease approaching members of staff about this matter. This is inappropriate and the integrity of the staff member could be brought into question.

Should you have any further concerns in respect to Leafy Knowe Care Home please do not hesitate to contact us through the proper channels. We are always happy to help.

S. Thurlow
Manager

Leafy Knowe © *With You All The Way*

****

KlevoPsychi©

04/03/20

KlevoPsychi© have been made aware of your recent concerns regarding KlevoPsychi©
EXICCO© pain management patches.

EXICCO© patches are the most advanced, powerful form of pain management in circulation. Endorsed by the NIHCE and MHPRA, KlevoPsychi© prides itself on an exemplary security record and is under continuous scrutiny, as are all British pharmaceutical companies.

The pain brought about by your wife's osteoporosis is carefully managed and much improved by the utilisation of EXICCO© patches. Your wife is Stage 4: CDR-2 so you will be aware that memory fluctuation is the preeminent symptom of dementia.

Please find attached the EXICCO© specification document. I trust you will find this satisfies your concerns and reassures you regarding further queries you may have in regard to EXICCO© patches.

KlevoPsychi© PO Box 386 London SW1E.

DIRECTOR OF THE PRESCRIPTION MEDICINES CODE
OF PRACTICE AUTHORITY

OUR REF: KLEV2EXI943-Bing

07/09/20

Dear Mr Bingham

Please find enclosed your returned correspondence.

We are reliably informed that your wife Mrs N. Bingham (229-aS1) is classed Stage 4: CDR-2 Dementia. This renders her incapable of coherent thought processes.

In addition, it is our duty to advise you that the recording of individuals can be considered a breach of that person's right to privacy and can result in an infringement of the Data Protection Act 1998. Refusal to comply with this ruling could result in prosecution.

Please do not hesitate to contact this office should you feel we can be of any further assistance.

PO Box 386 London SW1E

<u>TO WHOM IT MAY CONCERN</u>   3rd July 2020

My wife Nancy Bingham has been a resident of Leafy Knowe Care Home for almost two years. Her acute osteoporosis is being treated with Exicco patches which seem very effective.

I have however noticed an anomaly in my wife's deterioration in that there seems to be a pattern to her ability or inability to recall memories and one which displays extraordinary regularity. I have concluded that since being prescribed Exicco patches, these periods of memory loss can be tracked and even predicted. Illogical perhaps but I implore you to indulge this elderly gentleman.

Attached are three partial transcripts from several months of recordings. From these, one can observe how a memory is brought to the fore by our conversation. I chose three subjects of which Nancy has strong, embedded memories; our honeymoon, 1959, Frederick's death (Nancy's younger brother), 1932 and the pupils of St. Annes College. (Nancy was employed as a Botany teacher from 1956 to 1993).

Leafy Knowe Care Home has refused my request for information but I have revealed that the dates of patch removal coincides with the departure of visitors which in turn prompts permanent memory loss. This can no longer be considered coincidental, irrational as that may sound.

I hope you will agree that this issue warrants further investigation. I am deeply concerned for my wife and the other residents. It would be a desperate realisation to find there has been, in the least instance, an abuse of their trust and at worst something more sinister.

Sincerely
Dr. William D. Bingham (retired)

WEEK ONE - Transcript (excerpt) 10.06.20

Start   **1312**   **PATCH CHANGE 10.06.20:1443**
Finish   **1440**

N: Only me now Frederick's gone.

B: That was a long time ago Nancy you were only a child. You have me now remember? Bill. I'm not going anywhere.

N: Poor Frederick. Mother and Father became rimosed and ripe then passed as is the order but poor little brother endured barely a few short seasons perhaps he considered it a journey not worth taking we named him O'Kelly after the dactylorhiza fuchsii did you know that? Hello. Have you come to see me?

B: It's Bill, William. Do you remember our honeymoon Nancy, how warm it was?

N: Of course Bill, I'm not for the scrapheap just yet. Remember those silly straw umbrellas? Little bugs dropping into our food.. little flies...

B: Do you remember the sea, how beautiful it was...bright, bright blue?

N: Bright bright people argue over dactylorhiza fuchsii a separate species an indeterminate controversial variety and they argued over Frederick revolute as the air left his lungs flattened laevigate and leafless no one knew we named him O'Kelly and now there's no one left to give a hoot.

B: Do you remember the smell of the water Nancy?

N: It was lovely and warm wasn't it? I can feel it even now against my skin. And so clear you could see right to the bottom, see my feet as clear as day when there were flies at his mouth when he came here came to see me Bill there were flies at his mouth when he pulled pulled at my blouse.

B: [I waited for Nancy to settle].

N: Isn't the heat lovely? Feel it warming you all through, always lovely and warm in here, nice and cosy, so good of you to speak to me. Who are you here to see?

B: Alright dear, you rest.

(10.06.20:1440)

WEEK TWO - Transcript (excerpt) 17.06.20

Start   1327   **PATCH CHANGE   17.06.20: 1508**
Finish   1505

B: Do you remember the straw umbrellas on the beach in Majorca? We sat under them every day.

N: All those years gone Bill, a lifetime, just think of it.

B: The years certainly do pass Nancy.

N: I can't for the life of me imagine what I might have filled them with.

B: With a life Nancy. We've been lucky. Do you remember our honeymoon, in Majorca?

N: No. It worries me, don't remember things. Can't quite recall your name.

B: William.

N: And we were in Majorca?

B: Yes, on our honeymoon.

N: Our honeymoon? Oh my word so confused, this is all very confusing.

B: It doesn't matter dear. Can you remember St. Anne's? The children must all have children of their own now. Do you remember any of them Nancy?

N: Of course I do Bill. Every day for thirty seven years. One of them comes to mind. Victoria, everyone called her Tilly. Pretty little thing. There was Susan, her father was a kind man in spite of his wife a ghastly woman he still comes you know with his closed mouth and flies appear between his lips they squeeze through must live in his throat black but dry and feathery...

B: What did you teach at St. Anne's Nancy?

N: Oh Bill for goodness sake, why are you asking me that? Botany, you know that.

(17.06.20:1505)

WEEK THREE - Transcript (excerpt) 24.06.20

Start   1400   **PATCH CHANGE 24.06.20: 1531**
Finish   1527

B: I was thinking about St. Anne's this morning Nancy. Tilly and Susan, what characters they were.

N: Sorry, who are you?

B: It's me Nancy, Bill...do you remember when you were a teacher, the botany teacher at St. Anne's...the children, Tilly and Susan...

N: Don't know you. Who are you? Don't have children it's all lies and he'll be here and he'll proceed proceed with harvest and he won't like it that you're here he won't be happy to see you no and the flies will shoot from his lips and cling to the curtains and crawl into my hair...

B: Nancy stop. Please. Nothing is going to happen to you. You're safe here.

N: Bill.

B: Yes it's Bill, William. You know I often wonder what sort of a man Frederick would have turned out to be.

N: Frederick.

B: Frederick, your little brother, do you remember him Nancy.? O'Kelly, you named him O'Kelly, after a flower.

N: A soft echo of a seed beneath the peaty turf afraid there is no time now Frederick no time he'll be here soon for the harvest.

B: What's the harvest Nancy? Can you describe the harvest?

N: A brother? I have a brother?

B: Frederick. He's been dead a long time.

N: Dead a long time. You look nice today, it's nice to see you it gets lonely here and it's...
         [At this point a fly flew between us and distracted Nancy]

...it's the flies that tell me the flies squeezed from the mouth it's ligule lips cucullate and cladode and he will come again and he will harvest and he will empty the drupe of it's fruit and seed and the shells will dry and fall apart and return to the earth...

[At this juncture one of the Leafy Knowe Care Home staff approached and asked me to leave. The operative from the drug company had arrived and I wasn't permitted to remain with my wife.]

(24.06.20:1527)

Re: Dr William D. Bingham

KMedPractice (info@AMP.org)   20 Sept (2 days ago)
to KlevoP

To confirm that Dr. William D. Bingham has suffered a brain aneurysm leading to subarachnoid hemorrhage.

The consultant in attendance at the time of death declared no suspicious circumstances.

Dr Bingham leaves no family other than his wife Nancy who currently resides at Leafy Knowe Care Home.

M.T.
KMedPractice.

KMedPractice. PO BOX 324

He sits.

He takes a sip of water. He eases the flash drive into the port in his skull and closes his eyes.

The sun is lower. It appears to be cooler than before. The shadows of the schoolgirls are stretched and narrow. The limbs of the willow are still. The girl is standing in front of the viewer. Her skirt is raised. She reveals a mottled rash which sullies the otherwise unmarked flesh of her thigh. The woman's hand reaches out to her. It is holding something.
"*This should ease the stinging Tilly. Rumex obtusifolius.*'
Dark mossy streaks appear as a leaf is stroked across the girl's pale skin.
'*Thank you Mrs Bingham.*'

His arm is rigid, his hand reaching towards the girl, fingers gripped tightly. He feels her breath, the balmy softness, the beats, the pulse in his spine, the pressure in his groin.
'These are for you.'
Somewhere else, a young voice speaks.
'I got them on the beach.'
His body shudders and he lurches.

The girl smiles. Her eyes meet those of the viewer. The hem of her dress is lowered.

'You're hurting me.'

The crow wipes a hollow beak across the flat edge of a stone.

He opens his eyes. He lurches again. He sees his daughter. He sees fingers clenched around the flesh of her chest. They are his fingers.
'Daddy, you're hurting me.'

She is holding an armful of smooth pebbles against her childs body. He releases. He jerks and the pebbles drop, a violent discharge which cracks against the floor in a thunder.

His daughter runs from the room. He raises both hands to his head. He tears at the callous in his skull but it will never be enough, this his dishonest charade. He feels the pressure ease. He rests his hands across his lap, now languid, the echoes of plundered memories still playing within his skull.

WHY WICKED IS A LIE

REBECCA RAEBURN

People have an obsession with the past, and then they become it. Mine always belonged to Jodie and Michael. From an early age I had to learn how to become invisible, because when they looked at me they saw everything that came before me and they couldn't let it go.

I got used to manoeuvring the ridges of their arguments like a carefully choreographed dance, and for the most part it was bearable. Michael would disappear at night and return to the house a slur of skin and words and malt, and Jodie would howl like a wolf at the moon until morning.

They were always performing in those years, and I was the girl behind the curtain.

Owen Bardoch was my only way out. I used to think that he saw me when they never. Maybe it was the stones he'd carve behind the fig orchard in our cul-de-sac, the snowberries from his back garden that he'd pick and hand to me, or just the fact that he spoke to me without mentioning them, as though it never mattered.

I was under the assumption that he was different.

The summer we first started talking about leaving school and university was the same summer the dust road appeared in our town, entirely of its own accord. Owen said from the beginning that the road was the reason he knew he could probably love, but only probably, because when the road wasn't there, he couldn't possibly love anything. His chalky blue eyes buttoned in on themselves when he said that, as if they didn't belong to him anymore.

I ask him again to remind me why he can't love without the road. It's been months since we saw it for the first time, and since then everything has changed.

'Because of absence,' he says.

Then I nod and leave it at that. I'm sick of his shit.

Owen is the kind of person that kills you slowly by asking 'sorry?' after you've spent ten minutes trying to voice something you've been thinking about forever. Like the time I'd decided to tell him I was feeling tired, and not because I hadn't slept enough, but because I watched everything. I watched myself, inside and outside. I wanted to make sure that I wouldn't disappear completely.

When I don't say anything else, he pushes on.

'She pierced my heart, you know. The wicked one.'

I have to dig the uneven ridges of my nails into the half-moon lines in my palms to stop myself from erupting into flames there and then. It was never her intention to pierce his heart. That was all on him.

We'd been cycling when we found her the first time. Owen's tire had burst and it squealed over and over as if he'd run over a dormouse until we stopped. He spotted the houses at the same time as me. They were stone washed and run down, cracked by rotten ivy and covered in patches of mould that looked as if someone had dipped their hands in murky paint and smeared it everywhere. He began pulling a row of wooden slats away from the door to one of them. They rattled onto the dry ground, unsettling the dust.

'Stop moving things,' I said, aware that we were intruding. I'd read an article from the underside of one of Michael's newspapers, about a man in America who got shot for climbing into an abandoned warehouse. When they found out he was looking for a collar that belonged to his childhood dog, the authorities and the residents still blamed him.

'That's awful,' I'd said.

When Michael flipped over the paper he shrugged his shoulders, the way he always did, like it was only because the air around him was nipping at him. I looked at his eyes, at the curling red veins and the too open eyelids, then at the crystal glass beside his chair, and I remember wishing our world could have been written differently.

Owen ignored my warning and stepped through the freed entrance. He was dressed in Levi's and a T-Shirt I'd seen countless times over the years. Two wings sat over his shoulder blades – the transfers had started to peel, but they were the last things to disappear into the darkness of the house.

'You should listen,' I whispered to Owen, to myself, and then no one.

I followed him in. It was bare on the inside – a frayed, colourless rug trailed across the wooden floorboards and a table with two chairs and chewed legs sat tucked in the corner. Next to the doorway, somebody had etched uneven lines into the wooden skirting, marking height measurements. It reminded me of our house.

It was the kind of place that sucked time backwards.

When we stumbled back out into the daylight, that's when we saw her.

Her skin was pale but I had to blink because she was shimmering, but properly shimmering, the way the ocean does when the sun breathes on it and it stops being real. She never did tell us her name but I call her Day because whenever I think about that day she becomes it. The whole thing, and I forget that night even exists.

'Hullo!' Owen said in his clumsy voice. He started walking towards her with heavy steps and I wanted to throw out a rope and drag his ass back because she was going to run. She slid back about five steps. Her feet were naked and they left delicate prints in the road's dust.

'Stop walking, Owen,' I looked at him and when his eyes met mine he looked like he was going to cry.

'Where are we?' I asked Day.

She kept staring at us with these massive loris eyes that refused to blink.

'We're on the perimeter,' her voice trailed into the air and as it did a group of girls started to climb out of the places they'd been hiding in, spider-limbs bending over window-frames and misshapen rocks until they stood wavering like lights themselves.

Part of me wanted to tell Jodie and Michael about the girl we'd found on the road, but there was never a right time for me to appear back in their life. Each night had become consumed by their hapless theatrics. Michael was growing into his role with each passing sunset and I could see the yellow in his skin bruising like ripe fruit as he hid bottles in unworn boots and amongst the kitchen supplies. One day, I was sure, they'd fill the entire house and we'd spill out onto the streets as shipwreck.

Jodie was trapped too, but we had long since stopped being able to help one another. I was too good at being invisible, and she was bound by a vow she'd made in better days.

One time they rehearsed and rehearsed into the late hours of the night. I tried to listen through the crack in my bedroom door but I fell asleep. When I woke up it felt as though the house had finally sunk under the weight of their expectations and unintended memories. I got up and searched the rooms but nobody was there.

I resolved to run away myself, if only for a while, and for that I had needed Owen.

'Do you remember when we were supposed to go to Hersh's?' I ask Owen as we sit on the porch outside his front door. He knows that I've wanted to speak to him for a while now.

'Hmmm?' It's more a sound than a word.

'Where did you go when we were supposed to go to Hersh's?'

He scrapes the film of sweat from his forehead into his hair. 'I forget.'

It feels like more than a month ago, but I remember the way the sun trailed after us on our way out of town. We drove in silence at first and watched as the houses slowly thinned out and snaked through golden cornfields. Hersh lived by the coast three hours North, and Owen had brought Day up within the first half hour.

'She reminds me of someone,' his words broke the silence like popping candy.

'Why is this all you can talk about?'

'Because I think I know her.'

'Reminding you of someone is not the same as *being* that someone.'

'Doesn't she look familiar to you?'

I thought about it, I really did, but Day was entirely Day.

When I told him that he grunted and tried to pull his sunglasses from the glove compartment. The car swerved onto the grass embankment.

'Shit!' Owen shouted, forgetting the glasses. He pulled the wheel back towards him, righting the car, and then we both saw it. The road. The same one we'd found on our bikes. There were no signposts, just a narrow lane big enough for one car to squeeze through. A row of brittle bushes adorned either side – they dwindled out into the ground beneath them to reveal the flat land holding the bleached houses.

Owen stopped the car in front of them and pulled up the handbrake. When we climbed out of it we found Day in between the buildings. The other girls were there too, speaking quietly amongst themselves, and it was as though they'd mastered the art of whispering because the sound of their words drifted out and blew over the square like running water. Like echoes.

'You're back?' Day said to me and then turned her attention to Owen. He stood with his elbow touching mine, staring out at the other girls as if they were gold dust, as if he was searching for something he'd never been able to find.

'We're very protective of our home, it's taken us a while to build things back up.'

'Back up from what?' I asked.

She didn't answer, and I thought then that she was changing the subject. 'People have the tendency to expect the strangest things from love. Did you notice?' she asked, and the word love sounded wrong in that moment. It didn't belong there.

I thought about it, even though I didn't have to, and I wondered if Jodie and Michael would have noticed that I'd left the house without telling them. What would happen if I disappeared altogether and there was no trace left? Would that scene belong in their play?

'What's she talking about?' Owen asked. It sounded like he was shouting from across a field but his mouth was right next to my shoulder. 'Nothing makes sense here.'

Then all of a sudden he was burning. Right there in front of me. It started down by the soles of his feet, then licked up the marrow of his thighbones, coiled around his spine and into the hollow cavern of his ribcage, drowning out the beating of his heart. He was covered in deep purple flames but he wasn't screaming.

'I'm not staying. Are you coming?' he asked. I could barely hear him and when I made to answer he had already turned away, the sound of his car's engine drilling out beyond the stretch of road that led us there.

'He doesn't love you as much as you love him,' Day said, bowing her head so that her silver knotted hair scattered across her shoulders.

'I know – did you make him leave?'

She shrugged her shoulders, her lips curling into a strange smile that looked like a lie. And she *was* strange – impermanent like a border, thin and only just transparent enough to go unobserved by most. Yet somehow, when she'd stood on the road we'd broken down on, she'd been a night light plugged into the earth, glowing the way I'd wished I could glow when I was six and realised my skin was dull compared to the moonlight.

Day was not the past, like everyone else. She was something entirely different, and if she was wicked, then wicked was a lie.

'Why are you here?' she asked.

My eyelids felt like glue. 'I don't know.'

'Well, we trade in secrets here. Secrets for powers,' Day smiled gently then cast it amongst the other girls like breadcrumbs.

'What did you have to trade?'

'I forget,' she said. The sun's light was growing lazy, settling on the tips of the shattered glass still clinging to some of the window frames. Day closed her eyes for a second and then opened them right in front of mine. 'What do you see?'

I was looking at myself clearly, even clearer than in the reflection of a mirror. I looked older than I remember. I looked like flickering light bulbs and faded watercolour. But I was there and there was still so much breath in my eyes, and when I looked into them, I saw *her* – the one who would make everything worth it, and I fell in love. I fell in love with myself, with Day, and the child waiting behind her eyes. My lungs filled with time and the lack of it.

'What do you see?' she asked.

I could only speak when she closed her eyes.

'Everything.'

I knew without asking what it was that she would take. The only thing I had of mine that was worth giving. My invisibility. She placed my palm on top of hers and I watched as the small purple flames curled from hers into mine. I laughed out loud because it didn't just feel warm. It felt like strength.

Our written world has changed again since then. Jodie and Michael are drawing towards their final curtain call. Michael has been removed from stage, hidden in a sterile room with IV-drips and leads that should dilute the poison in his blood, but Jodie has seen this before, we all have, and the echoes of her own version of *O Fortuna* can be heard melting like butter into the walls of our home.

'I'm scared,' I tell Owen. 'I'm scared of what might happen.'

We move onto the grass from the porch so that we can lie on our backs. For a moment it feels like we might fall into the clouds above us. I hear Owen exhale beside me and I wish more than anything that he'd open his hand like he did when he was ten, revealing a small heart shaped rock that at least proves something.

Instead, he rolls over onto his shoulder so that he faces away from me. I count the number of words that he could say and find it doesn't hurt like it used to when they start building up. I keep counting. I uncurl my palm and stare at the small birthmark in its centre. Watch as it burns brighter and brighter until the flames curl around my arm and then twist away to wrap around the stranger by my side.

BLACKOUT

BLACKOUT

RICKY MONAHAN BROWN

My transfer to the Rusk Institute of Rehabilitation Medicine takes place on a Wednesday, three and a half weeks after the explosion in my brain. In one sense, the worst is over. In another, it's just beginning. My friends are concerned that the Ricky they knew is never coming back. Any recovery will be long and painful.

Meanwhile, storm clouds are gathering over New York.

The medical centres that make up the Rusk Institute are scattered around the city. An ambulance takes me to the Hospital For Joint Diseases at Second Avenue and Seventeenth Street in Manhattan. A grey monolith, its entrance is plunged into darkness by a canopy of blue plywood and scaffolding. A large, silver truck sits outside every day, unmoving, the doors to its main compartment plastered with ominous warning signs.

Inside the hospital, the corridors of the ninth floor are lined by long, blue counters facing wards that accommodate pairs of patients. Nurses sit facing the open doors of the wards so that the stroke patients and other victims of brain injuries who had somehow managed to avoid being put on a twenty-four hour watch can still be closely monitored. The nurses are lovely, and their faces burst into life when they are engaged, and when they are providing encouragement to patients. Unfortunately for them, they spend most of their days dealing with people who can't understand what is going on, or what has happened to land them in this place. When you catch a glimpse of a nurse, unaware, at one of the long blue counters, you can see the toll it takes.

It doesn't help that, at the time of my admittance, the HJD is being renovated. Although the wards themselves, with their shiny, polished blue floors, are spick and span, the corridors are lined with mysterious items of hospital equipment. Thick polythene sheets draped along the hallways make the shapes of things blurry and indistinct. The elevators move slowly. The voices of late night visitors and the pleas of the stricken float through scenes of dilapidation. Despite the efforts of the staff, there is something Kafkaesque about the scene, mirroring as it does the disarray and confusion in minds of the patients.

Each day, each change of shift, starts the same way. I am asked the usual set of questions. Things like, *What's your name?* and *How old are you?*

Most days, I know who I am. One day, I ask a passing resident doctor for some ice chips.

'Get me some ice chips! I'm a very important man! I'm going to be the vice-president!'

'Of what?' the young medic asks.

'Of the country, man! What do you think?'

Getting my age right is always difficult. My stroke occurred two weeks after my birthday, and that hadn't been enough time for my new age to take. I was like someone writing the wrong date on his cheques after the turn of the year. And as well as not being quite sure *when* I was, I couldn't say *where* I was. One day, another resident stands at the end of my bed and asks the questions. Beth sits in a hard plastic bucket seat, biting her nails and wincing with every inquiry.

'Do you know where you are?'

My eyes skitter back and forth as I scan the empty space in my head. I throw out a guess.

'A school?'

'No. Can you try again?'

'A building?'

I've given up. I just want this to be over. But she perseveres.

'What kind of building?'

'An office building?'

Beth tries to help. 'Have a look around,' she says.

I look around. Oh my god.

'Am I in a hospital?'

'Yes. You're in hospital. Do you know why you're here?'

My eyes moisten.

'Oh, god. Have I had another stroke?'

'No, Lover,' Beth reassures me. 'Just the one.'

Cable news runs on a TV on the wall at the far end of my new bed. By Sunday, they're talking about the *Frankenstorm*. Everyone in the city is talking about the *Frankenstorm*, and now it's permeated the therapeutic bubble that protects Rusk's patients. Hurricane Sandy – *Superstorm Sandy* – had started with a tropical wave in the Caribbean six days earlier. Now, the staff are talking about it and swapping the news they've heard, and the hospital's plans, with their friends at other institutions.

Sandy's latest, most ominous, designation was meant to evoke the joining of the hurricane with a second weather front as it approached the East Coast, to create a monster storm. As I lay crippled in bed, watching the news describe the six different levels of evacuation threat being assigned to city neighbourhoods, the word *Frankenstorm* roughly grabbed me by my delicate neural circuits. As Sandy approached New York, she did indeed appear increasingly monstrous. My experience of storm scares in the northeast had been that they would be talked up before blowing themselves out just off the coast. This time, the news reports talked of Sandy barrelling northwest towards New Jersey.

And this time, she did. As hour after hour of immaculately coifed, interchangeable anchors gleefully celebrated the fact that there was some real news to report, the rise of the waters in New York Harbor and the Gowanus Canal was mirrored by the rise of the anxiety in the topography of my brain. Throughout my stays in Methodist and Rusk, I was often agitated, and when this agitation descended, the nurses would hail Beth's arrival. When I saw her arrive, whatever was going on would blow away like a cumulis humilis, and a sunny smile would emerge as I exclaimed *Oh hi, Baby!*

But on the night of Sunday the 28th, the day before Sandy's arrival in the city, the Metropolitan Transport Authority shut the city's subway system. Beth left the office and went to Union Market to pick up some groceries before hunkering down. The experts were predicting that Sandy would sit over the metropolitan area for two or three days once she hit. They advised the populace to batten down the hatches, get supplies in, and prepare for the science that kept New York City running to be battered into the stone age. The power would be going down, the citizenry was warned. Cell phone coverage would fail.

By Monday, the storm had settled in the city like an ageing Scottish hipster and wasn't going anywhere. The Breezy Point neighbourhood of Queens was ablaze, after rising sea water flooded the electrics of a home in the area. One hundred and twenty-two homes were destroyed in that neighbourhood alone. The news was cataclysmic. Intrepid reporters stood on the Jersey Shore, being pelted by the waves pouring over the boardwalk. The Gowanus, just six blocks down the Park Slope from our apartment, and one of the most contaminated bodies of water in the United States, poured over its banks and into homes.

Then, there was a massive phosphoric flash at the ConEd substation on 14th Street on the West Side, clearly visible from across the river in Brooklyn. The blast looked deafening to the Brooklynites, even though nothing could be heard over the roar of the wind. A transformer had been flooded, and the resulting explosion knocked out the power below Midtown. Liquid had compromised the city and destroyed its functionality.

Up on 57th Street, a 150-foot crane boom spastically flapped to and fro in the winds, twisted and crumpled, uncontrollable, like a stroke patient's weak arm. Reporters worriedly admitted that nobody knew if the damaged limb could be brought under control before disaster struck, and it plunged a thousand feet onto a gas main. The power outages extended to Langone Medical Center at First Avenue at 30th Street on the East Side, where nurses were carrying newborns down nine flights of stairs so they could be transferred to a location with power.

At the Hospital for Joint Diseases, the back-up generator was operational, but no non-essential lights were operating. The two patients in Room 920, addled by the unfamiliarity of their situation even before Sandy hit, were plunged into their own personal Bedlam. Poor Alfonso, an 82 year-old man scared of the dark, demanded indignantly that power be restored. My mind raced in a perpetual, uncontrolled disquietude, and I begged to be allowed to use a phone. In the face of my ranting neighbour, I just needed to talk to my girlfriend, the nice girl with the brown hair and the glasses. She was clever and brave. She could persuade the staff to let me go home.

But the phones didn't work. I couldn't call Beth. She couldn't call me, and couldn't get any information online. For the only day during my stays at Methodist Hospital and then the HJD, she couldn't visit me.

Finally, Sandy relented, and the city haltingly checked the extent of the destruction, what was working. By Tuesday evening, Beth's fellow New Yorkers were still in their homes and the roads were empty, but she got a lift into town from Spanky. He was the ideal man for this job. An ear, nose and throat doctor, with a talent for facial reconstruction surgery, he was unflappable. With a banana suit in the trunk, he had the requisite irreverence. And, working a hundred hours a week, he was prone to falling asleep at the wheel and crashing – so empty streets were a good thing.

When they arrived, Beth and Spanky found me still awake, with the rattled Alfonso and our round-the-clock nurse for company. Spanky had to get back to Brooklyn, so they weren't able to stay for long in the dark. But the easy familiarity of my lover and her best pal was a salve after two days during which I had been plagued by terrible angels standing upon the sea and the earth, clothed in dark clouds, their feet as pillars of fire, their voices roaring like thunder along the claustrophobic downtown streets. I still wanted to go home, but Beth could only promise to come back the next day.

By Wednesday, downtown New York had spent days in darkness. The staff at the Hospital For Joint Diseases could no longer regulate the patients' body clocks with electric light. But the city was slowly coming back to life. Beth was expected back at work. Morgan Stanley's office in the Financial District would be out of commission for six weeks. The foyer of One New York Plaza conveyed the solidity and affluence of the typical late 20th century financial cathedral while eschewing ostentatious flash, all as required by tradition. A lustrous marble floor escorted the slap of leather brogues and the click of office heels past multiple security desks to various banks of elevators and escalators that ferried masters of the universe and their peons up to the offices and cubicles above and down to the Dunkin Donuts and the dry cleaners below. Ideally, there would be no need to leave the building to attend to sustenance or hygiene.

But now, the scene downstairs resembled something from a disaster movie. The cleaners and the doughnut chain store were completely submerged in floodwaters that reached the top of the basement stairs. Similar scenes were replicated across the city. There would be no power in the East Village for the balance of the week. The subways were still down. But even an act of god can't stop the gears of finance, so Beth had to report for work at One Pierrepont Plaza in Brooklyn. At least that was a little more local to our home. And the MTA had decreed that city buses would be free on Wednesday and Thursday. But with everyone going back to work, the subway out of action, and the city's petrol stations dry, the three mile trip from 15th Street took two hours.

It made for a shorter work day, though. Beth made it home to get ready to visit her stroke bloke, having arranged a lift from Matt, one of our buddies from Harry Boland's Bar. Fortunately, they had enough gas to make it to the hospital. Unfortunately, New York City was the world's biggest stroke patient. It's common knowledge that, if you have a stroke on one side of your brain, the opposite side of your body will be the weak side. But it's incredible how, if the stroke patient draws a line directly down the centre of himself, the delineation between the two sides is quite exact. One of the most worrying moments of my convalescence was waking up one morning, rubbing my eyes, and feeling the numbness in my left eye and eye socket. My two nostrils felt different for months, too. Not noticeably, most of the time, but certainly if I had a good dig around. Very occasionally and slightly, but perceptibly, my two balls felt different.

An iconic photograph covering *New York Magazine* in Sandy's aftermath painted Manhattan in a similar light. The view, from the southwest of the southern tip of the island, shows the Williamsburg Bridge, over which Beth and I had gleefully ridden our scooter weeks earlier, lit on the Brooklyn side, but the lights abruptly die halfway across the East River. A sharp diagonal line, running from 39th Street on the East Side to 26th Street on the West Side, separates those with power to the north from those in darkness below. Except, Battery Park City, just north of the Financial District, is illuminated. And above that, coated in Teflon and blazing like a beacon of *Freedom* – or as the political blog *Roadkill Refugee* tweeted at the time, a giant middle finger to the rest of New York – is Goldman Sachs Tower.

When Matt and Beth finished navigating the empty streets, unlit by street lamps or traffic lights, and reached the Hospital for Joint Diseases, they found that, like Goldman Sachs, it was running on its backup generator, at least to the extent of vital services. The lights in the corridors were on. Life support systems and monitors provided the only light in the wards.

Exhausted by his perpetual fury, Alfonso finally slept. Drained by the anxiety the storm had generated, and in the absence of any distracting activities, I was also asleep. The scene on the ninth floor was even more apocalyptic than usual, and my visitors stayed just long enough to pick up my latest batch of piss-stained clothes.

Then, on the morning of November the First, power was restored to Lower Manhattan. That afternoon, the lights went back on at the HJD. And with a pleasing symmetry, the lights went back on in my head.

A CHARM FOR THE WORLD AS IT IS

HELEN MCCLORY

A charm for autumn light, and your skirts sopping at the water's edge. A charm for raising your blood, so that you can walk, trailing dirt and leaves, away from the water and through the park. A charm for knowing history. A charm for silencing doubt. A charm for doubt. A charm for making a lie apparent. A charm for silencing the dull ache that returns to you as you remember everything the world is and still is and continues to be. A charm for your awful pain at it. A charm for your body's flesh that persists in being your flesh. A charm against the din of the nearing road. A charm for the people walking out of the fog and into your circle of damp misery. A charm against politically-induced depression. A charm against Brexit. A charm for compassion. A charm for autumn light. A charm for the buses, and the people on the buses, all normal and good folk, arms in slings, legs kicking against buggies, eyes blinking behind specs, heads bent over phones. A charm for them. A charm for the people you walk by, who are staring, of course they are staring, but doubt themselves for doing it and turning away and leaving you to this walk. A charm for doubt. A charm against Trump. A charm for faith in other people, even though. A charm for resisting. A charm for the last twigs to drop off your maxi dress, bought in a supermarket, the right weight, the pockets sagging. A charm for your exposure, your hands pressed against the algaed fabric. A charm for the people you walk by to let you pass unaided. A charm against escaped sobs. A charm against bewilderment at another's suffering, a charm for compassion. A charm for autumn light. A charm for the strength to witness the world. A charm against Neo-Nazis. A charm for the way past the processions of men. A charm for the way through the days of demagogues. A charm for making a lie apparent, a truth evident, a lie scaled and upended. A charm against powerlessness. A charm against the fact that magic does not exist. A charm against power, a charm that has no power, but. A charm for the corner shop and all who sail in her. A charm for a plant in a window with dust on it, and a small cat who sees you and opens its mouth. A charm against consuming as feeble rejoinder to a sense of powerlessness. A charm for living. A charm for the living. A charm for all the lives that will have to resist. A charm for knowing history. A charm for seeing which side blood is buttered. A charm for autumn light. A charm for crossing the road without getting hit. A charm for all Cassandras. A charm for walking away from the end. A charm for gentleness. A charm for the fight. A charm for the air, a charm written on air, and rewritten and always needing to be rewritten. A charm for every day. A charm against despair, and when it does come, for despair splitting like a frayed cord and sparking itself out to leave what is left, a cold feeling, less than content but fit to be retooled to other better use. A charm for autumn light. A charm for the room you left. A charm against the room you left. A charm for the two worlds on line and irl and more in which we live what is, and what we think it is. A charm for a lighter and a heavier heart. A charm against a hopeless future. A charm for frailty and continuing to fight. A charm for the world as it is, and your continuing to live in it.

Look out for Helen's new story collection

MAYHEM & DEATH

Coming March 2018, from 404 Ink

THE LAST DAYS OF

DAYS

JAMES SCYTHE

George Davies 📎
A new case: can we talk?
To: Lilly Banning

13:44
Details
GD

Dear Lilly,

I hope this email finds you well – it's been a while. How is everything? Last I heard, you'd moved into librarianship. Currently surrounded by reams of paper, I'm tempted to follow suit! I suspect the reading is a lot more fun...

I'll try not to take up too much of your time – there's been a surge of interest in a missing person's case that we'd like to get you back in for. The team noted that you worked closely with James Scythe for several years during your time here and his case has all authorities perplexed. We've been watching from afar since hearing of his disappearance, but something doesn't feel quite right. You knew him better than anyone else here – would you help us?

The team believe there's no one better to help find out what happened to one of our own, and are keen to get this underway as soon as possible.

What you are about to read is confidential and, I warn you now, unlike anything we've come across before.

Best wishes,

Greorge

George Davies
Director
Ombudsmen of the Preternatural

To: George Davies ⌄

Cc:

Bcc:

Subject: Re: A new case: can we talk?

Hi George,

The James Scythe
Case Files

Notes

_____
_____
_____
_____
_____
_____

OCTOBER 2014

THE PAGES WITHIN CONSIDER A WORLD IN WHICH
I HAVE FOUND MYSELF FALLING INTO, AND
NEED TO DOCUMENT SO THE WORLD KNOWS.

THOUGH, IF YOU'RE READING THIS, GOD ONLY
KNOWS WHAT'S HAPPENED TO ME. IF THIS IS IN
YOUR HANDS, DO WHAT YOU HAVE TO DO TO
MAKE EVERYONE UNDERSTAND.
I HOPE IT NEVER COMES TO THAT.

J. SCYTHE

WHAT HAPPENED TO JAMES SCYTHE?

What you are about to read is confidential. One of the Ombudsman of the Preternatural's former Special Agents went missing in 2015 and it's time to answer the question that the authorities have ignored: what happened to James Scythe? Many have tried to follow the unnatural and unsettling story of Southampton's prolific mystery but no one has been granted full access to the official James Scythe case files to piece together exactly what happened to him in his last days.

Until now.

Lilly will be back with her findings shortly. We trust you will keep this between us.

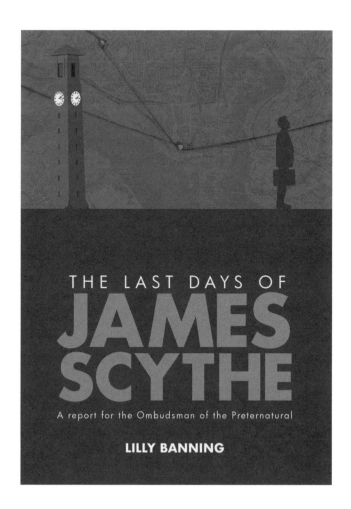

THE LAST DAYS OF
JAMES
SCYTHE
A report for the Ombudsman of the Preternatural

LILLY BANNING

BOOKS OF 2017

We decided to ask various 404 Ink authors to tell us their top books of 2017 in case you needed a few more recommendations! Okay, so, a little bit of cheating here: these are favourite books *read* in 2017, not necessarily published. We hope you'll find something new in here to see you through 2018.

SIM BAJWA, NASTY WOMEN:
Goblin – Ever Dundas
In Ever's gorgeous debut, we follow Goblin - jumping between the past and present - from childhood during the Second World War to living in 21st century Edinburgh. It's such a captivating, masterful exploration of trauma and identity, with dashes of the fantastical and subversive. Its unlike anything I've read before and know Goblin's story is going to stay with me for a long time.

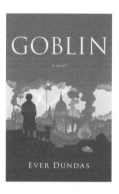

HELEN MCCLORY, MAYHEM & DEATH
(COMING MARCH 2018):
The Blue Fox – Sjon
The Blue Fox by Sjon introduced me to an Icelandic author who writes with a sly, economical, experimental brilliance. To summarise this short, aphoristic novel would probably be to destroy its pleasures. You can read it in a couple of hours. It will linger with you a lot longer.

CHRIS MCQUEER, HINGS:
This Is Memorial Device – David Keenan
So many of mates recommended this book to me and I definitely wasn't disappointed. It's one of the most original books I've ever read and I was drawn into this weird, dreamy version of 70s and 80s Lanarkshire and loved every minute of it. Funny, profound, psychedelic, haunting and totally exhilarating .

LAURA WADDELL, NASTY WOMEN:

Fever Dream – Samanta Schweblin

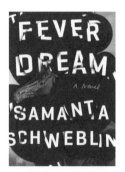

Fever Dream by Samanta Schweblin (translated by Megan McDowell) had a well deserved place on the Man Booker International shortlist. A shivering, sweating tale of bodily horror and environmental hazard, it's a suspenseful novella about a woman, her child, and their neighbours set in rural Argentina. I caught the fever and couldn't put it down.

REN ALDRIDGE, NASTY WOMEN:

The Outrun – Amy Liptrot

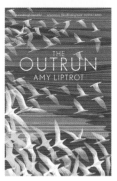

Whilst personal to her own story of struggling with alcoholism, Liptrot hits a raw place for anyone craving something beyond the party. She brings a literary and very human history of recovery in the natural landscape up to date, drawing her use of smart phone apps into her descriptions of navigating increasingly remote landscapes off the North Coast of Scotland. Affirming and relatable.

KRISTY DIAZ, NASTY WOMEN:

Hunger: A Memoir of (My) Body – Roxane Gay

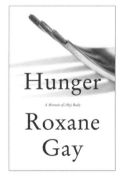

This book was released on my 30th birthday, marking a decade where society will (continue to) demand a lot from my body, a body I've never had a good relationship with. To read about Roxane Gay's relationship with hers is relatable in some ways, yet revelatory in others. I read it cover to cover in one sitting; its accessibility not detracting from the incisive ways in which it both broke and healed me.

BECCA INGLIS, NASTY WOMEN:

Women Walk the City in Paris, New York, Tokyo, Venice and London – Lauren Elkin

Three of my favourite things are the city, walking, and creative non-fiction, making Lauren Elkin's Flaneuse: Women Walk the City in Paris, New York, Tokyo, Venice and London a clear winner. Elkin writes a new (her)story of public spaces, weaving personal stories into anecdotes about Jean Rhys, Virginia Woolf, Parisian revolutions, New York suburbia, love, and war.

BEL OWEN, NASTY WOMEN:
Good Night Stories for Rebel Girls: 100 Tales of Extraordinary Women – Elena Favilli, Francesca Cavallo
A collection of stories aimed at younger readers, about 100 incredible women from artists to astronauts. This is my number one book this year because I had the privilege of gifting it to a friend's daughter and reading it through her eyes. Seeing how the stories could teach her, knowing she had so many strong role models. I like to think that it's her introduction to nasty women of the world and that one day she'll seek out her own intersectional feminist literature.

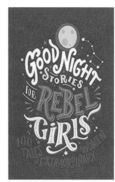

ZEBA TALKHANI, NASTY WOMEN:
Her Body and Other Parties – Carmen Maria Machado
Her Body and Other Parties by Carmen Maria Machado shifted something irreversibly within me. The book is a collection of intense stories, of women empowered and fragile, soft and brittle, scared and scary, all at once. The writing is the best I've read in a while, the words hitting me like shrapnel, cutting open parts of me I was too scared to touch.

MEL REEVE, NASTY WOMEN:
Autumn – Ali Smith
Set just after the EU referendum this books portrays the immediate, heart-breaking impact of Brexit as a backdrop to concerns about creativity, art, the state of the world and the nature of time. It's absorbing and moving - and at times chilling as you remember that this world she is depicting so masterfully is a reflection of the world around us now.

NADINE AISHA JASSAT, NASTY WOMEN:
The Hate U Give – Angie Thomas
The Hate U Give One of the best books I've read in a long time. THUG provides a brilliant and sharp insight into racism in the USA – from police violence and structural injustice, to the daily drip of microaggressions people of colour face. Perfectly weaving political truth with a compelling narrative and vivid characters, THUG will stay with you long after the final page.

CHRISTINA NEUWIRTH, NASTY WOMEN:
The Little Library Cookbook – Kate Young
This is my ideal book. It's beautiful, tells stories about stories, and stories about recipes. The instructions are easy to follow. Even reading the table of contents made me excited: the chocolate cake from Matilda! Green eggs and ham! Read it, look at it, cook from it.

The Little Library Cookbook
100 recipes from your favourite stories
KATE YOUNG

PICKS BY 404 INK

Why I'm No Longer Talking to White People About Race – Reni Eddo Lodge
In 2014, Reni Eddo-Lodge wrote a blog entitled 'Why I'm No Longer Talking to White People About Race'. Her words hit a nerve, and so her book was born, a vital exploration of eradicated black history to white-washed feminism, the links between class and race, and more. This is a vital book on what it is to be a person of colour in Britain today, and is a book you really must read.

Know Your Place – Edited by Nathan Connolly
Know Your Place is an essay collection about the working class, by the working class. Twenty four writers in Britain examine representation, literature, sexuality, gender, art, employment, poverty, childhood and more. A really excellent collection on what it means to be drawn from the bottom of Britain's archaic, but persistent, class structure, from those who live it.

This Is the Noise That Keeps Me Awake – Garbage
Garbage are known around the world for songs that mix pop sweetness with the dour thunder of industrial music and the rhythm punch of hip-hop. This Is The Noise That Keeps Me Awake features rare photos, personal snapshots, and follows the world and life of Garbage and their music in a beautiful, luminous pink package. Must have for Garbage fans.

The Power – Naomi Alderman

The world remains a recognisable place, but something vital has changed: teenage girls now have immense physical power – they can cause agonising pain and even death. And, with this small twist of nature, the world changes utterly. This is a fantastic book which flips the genders in terms of power and status, but also explores women's ability to electrocute people in interweaving narratives. Shockingly good (sorry, not sorry).

Hi-Fi Fight Club – Carly Usdin, Nina Vakueva

It's New Jersey. 1998. Chris starts her dream job: working at Vinyl Mayhem, her local record store. She's ready to deal with misogynistic metalheads, grunge wannabes, but she wasn't prepared for the news that her indie record store is actually a front for a teen girl vigilante fight club. It is basically amazing.

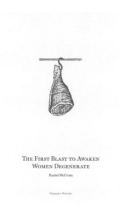

THE FIRST BLAST TO AWAKEN
WOMEN DEGENERATE

Rachel McCrum

Freight Poetry

The First Blast to Awaken Women Degenerate – Rachel McCrum

Spoken word queen Rachel McCrum released her debut poetry collection The First Blast to Awaken Women Degenerate this year and we love it. Before getting the chance to read it, we saw Rachel perform several poems live and they have such ferocity and playfulness, depending where you dip in. Rachel is magnificent, and her poetry equally so.

BIOGRAPHIES

CONTRIBUTOR BIOGRAPHIES

Sim Bajwa is a writer based in the West Midlands. Her work has previously been featured in *Fictionvale*, *Helios Quarterly*, the Dangerous Women Project, 404 Ink's *Nasty Women*, and will be a part of Fiction & Feeling's upcoming *Becoming Dangerous* anthology. She is currently working on her first fantasy novel.

Henry Bell is a writer and editor from Bristol, working on poetry and theatre. He lives on the Southside of Glasgow and edits *Gutter Magazine*. He was a Clydebuilt Poet and has edited books including *A Bird is Not a Stone*.
@henbell / henryjimbell.com

Andrew Blair is a poet. He is mostly motivated by jealousy. It takes him a long time to find joy in his friends and peers' successes. He asked me to write this bio because he trusts me and I am more popular than him.

Ricky Monahan Brown suffered a catastrophic hemorrhagic stroke in 2012. One version of that story is Nerd Bait's flash musical, The Treacherous Brain. 'Blackout' is an adapted extract from a survival memoir called *Stroke: A Love Story*. Or maybe *You Had An Orgasm, I Had a Stroke*. He hasn't decided.
@ricky_ballboy / @InterrobangEdin / @NerdBaitBand
apoplectic.me / interrobang.scot / nerdbaitband.com

Glasgow-based writer **Karyn Dougan** was 2016's New Writers Callan Gordon Award Winner. She has written for The List, The Skinny and The Bear, and has worked in almost every section of the book industry as a proofreader, editor, reviewer and bookseller. Her first short story was published in *Alight Here: An Anthology of Falkirk Writing* (Cargo, 2015).

Ever Dundas is a writer specialising in the weird and macabre. She writes literary fiction, horror, fantasy and sci-fi. Her first novel, *Goblin*, is about an outcast girl growing up in London during World War II. Ever is currently working on her second novel, *HellSans*, a sci-fi thriller, for which she received Open Project Funding from Creative Scotland.
@everdundas / www.everdundas.com

Siobhan Dunlop is a writer, poet, and book blogger who works in a library and is mostly fuelled by excessive varieties of tea. Currently working on a novel and dreaming of writing an epic poem to match Byron.
@fiendfull / fiendfullyreading.tumblr.com

Ryan Ende was forged in the frigid wastes of Western New York. He has received degrees in writing from Ithaca College and the School of the Art Institute of Chicago. When not delving into his writing world of superheroes, he can be found drinking or gaming on tabletops and Xboxes.
@EndeWrites

Jane Flett is a philosopher, cellist, and seamstress of most fetching stories. She has writing in the Best British Poetry, on BBC Radio 4, and at the Edinburgh International Book Festival. She's one half of the riot grrl band Razor Cunts, and a recipient of the Scottish Book Trust New Writer Award.
janeflett.com

Melissa Carmack Goodbourn grew up in North Carolina and now lives by the sea in Dunbar. Her writing often reflects her experiences growing up in the South, and at times, her political outrage. She has performed at Coastword Festival and the Callandar Poetry festival.

Caroline Grebbell spent fifteen years working in the TV and film industry before taking a year out to complete an MA in Creative Writing at Edinburgh Napier University in 2015. Since then she have been writing short stories, one of which – 'Model Organisms' – was nominated for a British Science Fiction Association Short Story award. She organised and hosted the International Women's Day 'Women in Sci-Fi' event for *Shoreline of Infinity* journal and is presently (with artist collaboration) preparing a full length graphic novel script for submission to publishers.

Darren Hepburn is a journalism student in Fife and has been writing fiction for as long as he can remember. @DarrenJHepburn

Stuart Kenny is an adventure travel journalist with Mpora, the biggest action sports website in Europe. He is also a regular face on the Edinburgh poetry scene, having performed with Loud Poets, Interrobang and more, and is now doubting whether or not he actually needed to write his bio in the third person.
@Stuartkenny

Veronique Kootstra is originally from the Netherlands but writes and dreams in English. She loves the challenge of flash fiction but has recently started exploring longer forms and is working on her first novel. She is part of the Write Like a Grrrl community. @vkootstra

Kirsty Logan is the author of the novels *The Gracekeepers* and *The Gloaming*, and the story collections *A Portable Shelter* and *The Rental Heart*. This story is from her forthcoming story collection, *The Night Tender*, a collection of horror stories about domestic fears.
@kirstylogan / kirstylogan.com

Jonathan Macho is an English Literature Graduate from Cardiff with an endless appetite for nonsense and a grudging friendship with a talking space raccoon. You can read his work in Candy Jar Books' *Beneath the Surface* Anthology, *404 Ink* and Chris Fielden's *To Hull and Back* 2015 and 2016.

Calum L MacLeòid was born in Inverness and now lives in Montréal. His first novel *A' Togail an t-Srùbain* was released by CLÀR in October 2017. He also writes the Gaelic column for The National.
@CalumMacLeoid

In his career as a writer, broadcaster and musician **Gary Marshall** has been heckled, bottled, threatened, harassed, molested, mocked in national newspapers, electrocuted, ripped off, chased by screaming teenagers and set on fire, although not all at the same time. Gary came out as transgender in early 2017.
@garymarshall / www.bigmouthstrikesagain.com

Matthew Meyer is the writer of the essay, 'The Basic Structure for a Story', which can be viewed atauthorspublish.com/the-basic-structure-for-a-story. He has also self-published a children's book series entitled, *Raising Hare*. He's also written for a Good Samaritan Society newsletter and has received his diploma in Creative Writing.
facebook.com/MatthewMeyerAuthor

Ross McCleary is from Edinburgh and has been published in *Pushing Out The Boat, Riddled With Arrows, Pop To,* and *Structo*. His novella, *Portrait of the Artist as a Viable Alternative to Death*, was published in 2016 by Maudlin House and shortlisted for a Saboteur Award.
@strongmisgiving

Helen McClory has a PhD in literature and creative writing from the University of Glasgow. Her debut story collection *On the Edges of Vision* won the Saltire First Book of the Year Award and her debut novel *The Flesh of the Peach* was released in early 2017. Her second story collection *Mayhem & Death* will be published by 404 Ink in 2018

Rebecca Monks is an award-winning author, playwright and journalist living in Edinburgh. Her fiction has appeared in *The List*, *Dirty Press* and *Freak Circus*, and she is a regular on the Edinburgh spoken word scene. She has had plays produced on the West End in London and the Edinburgh Fringe, and she has had bylines in The I, The List, The Scotsman, Scotland on Sunday and more. She is currently working on her debut novel.
@Rebecca_Monks / www.rebeccamonks.com

Lisa Parr is a writer from London and **Isaac Wilcox** is an artist from Glasgow. They have been making comics together from 2016 and have published a number of graphic short story zines that are available at independent book shops in Glasgow and Edinburgh.

Joseph S. Pete (@nwi_jsp) is an Iraq War veteran, an award-winning journalist and an Indiana University graduate. He was poet laureate of Chicago BaconFest, a feat that Chaucer chump never accomplished. His work has appeared in *Prairie Winds*, *The Grief Diaries*, *Tipton Poetry Journal*, *Dogzplot*, *shuf-Poetry*, *The Roaring Muse*, and elsewhere.

Rebecca Raeburn is based in Edinburgh and has an MSc in Creative Writing from the University of Edinburgh. She was shortlisted for the 2017 Alpine Fellowship Writing Prize and the Scottish Book Trust's New Writers Awards in 2016. She is currently working on her first novel and a collection of interrelated short stories.

Mel Reeve is an archivist and writer. She has contributed poetry to a variety of zines and publications, and recently had a personal essay published in 404 Ink's successful *Nasty Women* anthology. She is also part of Fear of Making Art Press, a small press based in central Scotland, and The Respite Room – a support project and community for people living with mental health problems.
@melreeve

Daniel Shand is a writer based in Edinburgh. His debut novel, *Fallow*, was shortlisted for the 2017 Betty Trask Prize. @danshand / daniel-shand.com

Siobhan Shields, a writer, poet and filmmaker, has been published via the Dangerous Women Project and Word-o-Mat. She has read her work at the Edinburgh International Book Festival and Edinburgh Fringe. Her award winning film 'Diane' was screened at the US Twin Peaks Festival and festivals in London and Malta.
@Siobhan_Shields

Carol Stewart is a mother of seven living in the Scottish Borders. A former freelance editor, she has only recently started out on her poetic journey and has so far had a poem shortlisted for the Eyewear fortnightly prize.

Bidh **Marcas Mac an Tuairneir** a' fuireach ann an Dùn Èideann, far a bheil e na thagraiche ollamhachd aig Oilthigh Dhùn Èideann. Tha e air dà cho-chru-inneachadh bàrdachd fhoillseachadh: *Deò* (Grace Note Publications, 2013) is *Lus na Tùise* (Clò a' Bhradain, 2016). B' e Dràmaire Ùr na Bliadhna, ann an 2016.

Marcas Mac an Tuairneir lives in Edinburgh where he is a PhD candidate in the Celtic Department at the University of Edinburgh. He has published two collections: *Deò* (Grace Note Publications, 2013) and *Lus na Tùise* (Bradan Press, 2016). He was named Gaelic New Playwright of the year in 2016.

THANK YOU!

THANK YOU TO OUR PATRONS

One year on, we still send our thanks to patrons new and old. Here's to those of you who support us and new writing on Patreon, whether you were there back in mid-2016 or only recently. We salute you.

Nicola Balkind
Russell Barker
Michelle Beauchamp
Chris Boyland
Alistair Braidwood
Nicole Brandon
Simon Brown
Charlene Busali
Caroline Clarke
Sean Cleaver
Suzanne Connor
Catriona Cox
Muireann Crowley
Paul Dettman
John Dexter
Doro
Gwendlyn Drayton
Finbarr Farragher
Madeleine Fenner
Liz Fox
Tom Gillespie
Sinèad Grainger
Rod Griffiths
Robbie Guillory
Kris Haddow
Rosie Howie
Michaela Hunter
Jamie Norman
Peter Kerr
Rebecca Kleanthous

Kirstin Lamb
Marek Lewandowski
Dean M Gardland
Paul M. Feeney
Madi
Susan McIvor
Mairi McKay
Kerry McShane
Sabrina Melojer
Juliette Morris Williams
Daiden O'Regan
Amanda Palmer
Stephen Paton
EK Reeder
Robert Clyde
Iain Ross
Simon Rowberry
Malin Rozon
Paula S Carr
Victoria Sinden
Kirstyn Smith
Claire Smith
Claire Squires
Kirsty Stanley
Elizabeth Stanley
Emma Swann
Nicole Sweeney
Jean Teather
Inside The Bell Jar
Eleanor Walker
Kristin Walter
Aran Ward Sell
Mark Wightman
Stevie Williams
Samanatha Wilson
Claire Withers
Ashley Wyse
Emma Zetterström

And a number of patrons who choose to remain anonymous.

SUBSCRIBE TO 404 INK

If you enjoyed this issue of *404 Ink*, would like to be signed up for the next, and receive all the gossip and info about upcoming publications first, then Patreon is the place to be!

How does Patreon work?

So glad you asked. On Patreon you pledge to give a creator a chosen amount of money either per month or per creation. We currently have our Patreon set up so we receive all pledges when the magazine issue is complete and ready to be sent out to readers. This is twice a year, in November and May.

You can pledge $1 to receive all the behind-the-scenes updates before anyone else, $5 for the ebook, $10 for the printed magazine (UK only) or $20 for the printed magazine if you're outside of the UK. (Patreon is a US company so pledges are in dollars, but they convert the currency, and it works wherever you are in the world!). All patrons are the first to hear about any news or reveals we may have.

When we're ready to send the magazine to subscribers we press the big red button which will send all pledged money to us – unlike normal subscriptions, we don't see any money until the magazine's ready, so you're not paying for anything until we have it ready for you in all its glory.

So why Patreon?

We're using Patreon because it's a public platform that brings transparency and accountability to the creative process. It means we have a direct relationship with our readers, we know that there's money coming in to help us pay our authors and it spreads the word about all those talented folks. We hope you'll hop on board.

www.patreon.com/404ink

GOODBYE